ENIGMA

CREATED BY
PETER MILLIGAN
DUNCAN FEGREDO

PETER
MILLIGAN
WRITER

DUNCAN
FEGREDO
ARTIST

SHERILYN
VAN **VALKENBURGH**
COLOR ARTIST

JOHN
COSTANZA
LETTERER

ENIGMA

Published by DC Comics. Cover and compilation copyright © 1995
DC Comics. All Rights Reserved.

Originally published in single magazine form as ENIGMA 1-8.
Art and text trademark and copyright © 1993 by Peter Milligan
and Duncan Fegredo.
All Rights Reserved. The stories, characters, and incidents
featured in this publication are entirely fictional.

DC Comics, 1700 Broadway, New York, NY 10019
A division of Warner Bros. - A Time Warner Entertainment Company
Printed in Canada. First Printing.
ISBN: 1-56389-192-1
Cover painting by Duncan Fegredo

SERIES

ORIGINALLY, THIS INTRODUCTION TO THE COLLECTED EDITION OF ENIGMA WAS TO HAVE BEEN WRITTEN BY NONE OTHER THAN GOODY TWO-SHOES, THE DANDY HIGHWAYMAN HIMSELF, MR. ADAM ANT. WHEN, HOWEVER, ANT WAS UNABLE TO MEET THE BRUTAL DEADLINE, GLAMOROUS EDITOR ART YOUNG WAS FORCED TO PLUNGE DOWN-MARKET IN SEARCH OF SOME SHAMELESS TART WHO'D BE WILLING TO WRITE *ANYTHING* FOR A COUPLE OF BUCKS — HENCE *ME*, SCANT SECONDS BEFORE PUBLICATION, HARASSED BUT IMMACULATE, TRYING TO PUT TOGETHER SOMETHING WHICH AT LEAST LOOKS AND SMELLS LIKE AN INTRODUCTION, EVEN IF IT DOESN'T TASTE LIKE ONE.

NAKED

BELIEVING, AS I DO, THAT NO INTRODUCTION EVER MADE *ANYONE* WANT TO BUY OR READ A BOOK, I WILL SIMPLY ATTEMPT TO GET THIS BUSINESS OVER AND DONE WITH AS QUICKLY AS IS HUMANLY POSSIBLE AND USING ANY MEANS NECESSARY. IF THIS INVOLVES ADOPTING THE OILY, UNCONVINCING TONES OF A PRACTICED TOASTMASTER PRESIDING OVER YET ANOTHER "CELEBRITY ROAST," THEN SO BE IT. THIS BOOK IS ABOUT THE TRUTH, THE TRUTH EVEN, AND ISN'T IT THE TRUTH OF THINGS THAT INTRODUCTIONS TO BOOKS ARE DESIGNED SOLELY TO PLACE UNDUE STRESS UPON THE SAINTLY HEADS OF THOSE CONDEMNED TO WRITE THEM? THE TRUTH *IS* THAT IT'S FAR TOO CHALLENGING A PROPOSITION TO HAVE TO FILL THIS SPACE WITH SOME KIND OF CRITICAL APPRAISAL OF ENIGMA, SO INSTEAD I'D PREFER TO TAKE THIS OPPORTUNITY TO PULL ASIDE THE SHOWER CURTAIN OF FAME AND REVEAL A GLIMPSE OF THE NAKED PETER MILLIGAN, THE PRIVATE MAN BEHIND THE PUBLIC MASK.

STRANGE

PERHAPS I SHOULD BEGIN MY RAMBLE BY STATING MY CREDENTIALS IN THIS AREA: I'VE BEEN ENJOYING PETER FOR SOME TIME NOW, IN A MANNER OF SPEAKING,

HAVING FOLLOWED HIS WORK — AS DAY FOLLOWS NIGHT AND CHAPMAN FOLLOWED LENNON — FROM THE GLORIOUS VISIONARY SPRAWL OF **STRANGE DAYS**, THROUGH HIS VARIOUS COLLABORATIONS WITH THE DIVINE BRENDAN MCCARTHY AND ON TO **SHADE, THE CHANGING MAN** ETC. ETC. DURING THAT TIME IT HAS BEEN MY PRIVILEGE (OR PERHAPS "FATE" WOULD BE THE MORE APPROPRIATE WORD), TO HAVE COME TO KNOW THE MAN HIMSELF AND IF NOT TO HAVE ACTUALLY SHARED HIS TRIUMPHS AND TRAGEDIES, TO AT LEAST HAVE HEARD ABOUT THEM ON THE PHONE VIA SOME THIRD PARTY OR OTHER.

B O W E L

MY MOST CHARMING MEMORIES OF PETER DATE FROM THAT HAUNTED SPRING OF 1992, WHEN HE AND I WERE INVITED TO ATTEND THE LUCCA COMICS CONVENTION IN NORTHERN ITALY. AS FOREIGN GUESTS, FLOWN ACROSS EUROPE AND HOUSED IN THE FINEST OF HOTELS, WE WERE NATURALLY EXPECTED TO REPAY THE HOSPITALITY OF OUR HOSTS BY MAKING SOME EFFORT TO ATTEND THE CONVENTION. AS INCORRIGIBLE LAYABOUTS, OF COURSE, IT WAS OUR INTENTION TO DO NOTHING WHATSOEVER WHICH HAD ABOUT IT THE SLIGHTEST WHIFF OF COMIC BOOKERY. SOMEHOW, WE MANAGED TO CONVINCE OUR ITALIAN FRIENDS THAT THE SHORT FLIGHT FROM LONDON TO PISA HAD SO CRIPPLED US WITH JET LAG THAT WE WERE ALL BUT INCAPABLE OF SPEECH AND MOVEMENT. WE FOUND THAT THE WORD "DIZZY" WORKED BEST WHEN WORMING OUR WAY OUT OF OUR OBLIGATIONS. WE LEARNED TO INVEST THE CONCEPT OF "DIZZINESS" WITH THAT SENSE OF DREAD AND FATALITY NORMALLY RESERVED FOR BOWEL CANCER.

ANOTHER DRUNKEN DAY LAZING IN THE HOTEL. A HOPEFUL ITALIAN VOICE ON THE TELEPHONE.

"WE HAVE A FILM CREW WAITING HERE TO INTERVIEW PETE MILLIGAN. IT'S FOR ITALIAN TV. IT'S REALLY QUITE IMPORTANT..."

I LOOK ACROSS TO WHERE PETER LOUNGES. HE SHAKES HIS HEAD, WAVES A DISMISSIVE HAND, PICKS UP HIS DRINK.

"I'M AFRAID PETE'S NOT FEELING TOO WELL RIGHT NOW. HE'S VERY DIZZY TODAY."

"AH...DIZZY...I'M SO SORRY TO HEAR THAT..."

DOWN GOES THE PHONE.

OR WHAT OF MILLIGAN, DERANGED BY DRINK AND DRUGS, STANDING ON THE ROCKS AT LERICI, WHERE THE POET SHELLEY DROWNED IN 1822? I DON'T BELIEVE I SHALL EVER BE FREE OF THE POIGNANT MEMORY OF MY FRIEND STAGGERING ONTO THE ROCKS, SHAKING HIS FIST AT THE INSENSIBLE WAVES AND SCREAMING "DO YOUR WORST, YOU BASTARDS! YOU'VE HAD SHELLEY BUT YOU WON'T HAVE ME!" NOR CAN I OVERLOOK HIS WORK WITH CHARITY, HIS GENTLENESS, GENEROSITY AND CHASTITY...

S T R I P

BUT YOU WANT THE TRUTH, DON'T YOU? AND I CAN'T KEEP UP THIS PETER USTINOV BOLLOCKS FOR VERY MUCH LONGER. THE TRUTH IS THAT LIES ARE OFTEN MORE HONEST THAN THEY'D LIKE TO BE. THE TRUTH IS THAT FICTION OFTEN TELLS US MORE ABOUT OURSELVES THAN WE'D PREFER TO KNOW. THE TRUTH IS THAT ENIGMA IS ONE OF THE GREATEST COMIC STRIP SERIES EVER WRITTEN BECAUSE, WITH VICIOUS GLEE, IT EXPOSES THE ABSURDITIES AND INADEQUACIES OF OUR LIVES AND HOLDS ALL OF OUR LUDICROUS HOPES AND FEARS UP TO THE HARSH LIGHT OF THE TRUTH. IT SHOWS US THE HUMAN CONDITION AS A CONDITION VERY MUCH LIKE DANDRUFF, BUT IT DOESN'T JUST STOP THERE. ENIGMA HAS BEEN DESCRIBED AS AN EXISTENTIALIST COMIC BUT I THINK IT'S MORE THAN THAT; LET'S FACE IT, WHEN WAS THE LAST TIME YOU HAD A GRIN WITH JEAN-PAUL SARTRE? THE GLEEFUL VICIOUSNESS OF THE HUMOR IN ENIGMA IS SUCH THAT NOT ONLY DOES IT MAKE US LAUGH, NOT ONLY DOES IT MAKE US CRINGE IN RECOGNITION AT THE PALTRINESS OF HUMAN DESIRES AND AMBITIONS, IT ALSO SHOWS US HOW WE CAN BECOME FREE, LIKE MICHAEL SMITH, BY NOT BEING AFRAID OF THE TRUTH.

AND ALL THIS IN A COMIC TOO!

B O T T O M

IN TERMS OF SHEER TECHNICAL BRAVADO, WHICH I DON'T EXPECT ANYONE BUT OTHER WRITERS TO GIVE A FLYING FART ABOUT, ENIGMA BREAKS NEW GROUND IN

EVERY CHAPTER. I COULD GO ON ALL DAY ABOUT THE INNOVATIVE SCENE TRANSITIONS AND CHARACTER BITS MADE POSSIBLE BY THE BRILLIANT DEVICE OF AN OMNIPRESENT CYNICAL NARRATOR (WHO, DESPITE HIS CONTEMPT FOR IT, CANNOT DISENTANGLE HIMSELF FROM THE TEXT IN WHICH HE IS AS DEEPLY EMBEDDED AS THE CHARACTERS HE RIDICULES SO EXQUISITELY). THE IDENTITY OF THE NARRATOR, CONCEALED UNTIL THE CLOSING PAGES, IS FINALLY REVEALED IN WHAT IS, FOR ME, THE SERIES' TRANSCENDENT MOMENT; A MOMENT WHICH RIPS THE LID OFF THE FICTIONAL WORLD JUST AS SURELY AS THE SKY IS TORN FROM THE ENIGMA'S WORLD AT THE BOTTOM OF A WELL IN ARIZONA.

VIBRANT

LET'S NOT FORGET THAT ENIGMA IS ALSO A SUPER-HERO COMIC AND PROVES THAT, DESPITE INSISTENCES TO THE CONTRARY, THERE ARE STILL ENDLESS POSSIBILITIES OPEN TO ANYONE WILLING TO PUT SOME TIME AND INTELLIGENCE INTO GRAPPLING WITH THE IDEAS RAISED BY ONE OF THE GREAT AMERICAN ARTFORMS. ENIGMA IS ABOUT SUPER-HEROES AND THE ORDINARY PEOPLE WHO MAKE SUPER-HEROES AND ABOUT THE REASONS WHY THEY DO IT. IT'S WORKING WITHIN A MARGINALIZED ART-FORM AND USES THE CLICHÉS OF THAT ARTFORM TO PRODUCE SOMETHING THAT'S MORE VIBRANT, MORE RELEVANT, MORE INCISIVE AND, FRANKLY, A GOOD DEAL MORE FUNNY THAN THE LATEST HYPED-UP NOVEL FROM THE LATEST THIN-BLOODED LITERARY SENSATION.

AROUSING

AND JUST IN CASE DUNCAN FEGREDO'S FEELING LEFT OUT AS I NEAR THE END OF MY PICARESQUE JOURNEY, HERE'S A BIT ABOUT HIM:

I HAVE WORSHIPPED THE BUST OF DUNCAN FEGREDO SINCE 1991 WHEN HE PAINTED MY KID ETERNITY SERIES FOR DC. (NO MEAN FEAT FOR THE HOPELESSLY COLORBLIND FEGREDO, WHO LIVES IN HIS OWN MAD WORLD - A WORLD NOTHING LIKE OUR OWN, WHERE FIRE ENGINES ARE ROYAL BLUE AND THE SKY IS A BLUSHING PINK.) HIS PEN AND INK WORK, SHOWCASED FOR THE FIRST TIME IN ENIGMA, IS EVERY BIT AS SEXUALLY AROUSING AS HIS KID ETERNITY ART BUT WITH THE ADDED BRILLIANCE OF

TER MILLIGAN & DUNCAN FEGREDO.
CALC92

INCREASINGLY SKILLFUL DRAFTSMANSHIP. DUNCAN REINVENTED HIMSELF IN THE PAGES OF ENIGMA AND PRODUCED HIS MOST EXPRESSIVE, MOST EXPLOSIVE WORK TO DATE. THERE'S ENOUGH LIBIDO HERE TO LIGHT UP BROADWAY, AND I SERIOUSLY URGE THE GOVERNMENTS OF THE WORLD TO CONSIDER USING DUNCAN FEGREDO AS AN ALTERNATIVE ENERGY SOURCE. CHEAP, CLEAN AND FRIENDLY? WELL, ONE OUT OF THREE'S NOT TOO BAD.

CLIMAX

AND HAVING DONE THAT, I SHOULD ALSO BRING TO YOUR ATTENTION THE COLORING OF SHERILYN VAN VALKENBURGH, WHICH BRINGS DUNCAN'S ARTWORK TO EVEN MORE VIVID AND WRITHING LIFE, IF SUCH A THING CAN BE COUNTENANCED. THE APOCALYPTIC CLIMAX OF CHAPTER 7 SHOWS JUST HOW MUCH OF THE CREDIT FOR THE MOOD OF THIS SERIES CAN BE LAID AT THE DOOR OF SHERILYN AND HER MAGIC BRUSHES. ADD TO THAT THE ELEGANT LETTERING OF JOHN COSTANZA AND THE DISTINCTIVELY *LOUCHE* EDITING OF ARTHUR YOUNG, AND YOU HAVE A LANDMARK, MATE, A BLEEDIN' *LANDMARK*, OF A COMIC SERIES AND SURELY THE ONLY CONTENDER FOR NEXT YEAR'S "BEST COLLECTION" AWARD.

SHAME

AND SO I REACH THE END. I HAD A DUTY, WHICH I DISCHARGED TO THE BEST OF MY ABILITY, AND MUST NOW WITHDRAW. IT WOULD BE A SHAME TO STAND IN THE WAY FOR EVEN A SECOND LONGER, AND THIS SCHOLARLY TONE OF VOICE CAN BECOME SO *ANNOYING* SOMETIMES.

ENIGMA IS MUCH, MUCH BETTER THAN I COULD EVER MAKE IT OUT TO BE. STOP READING THIS NOW. READ ENIGMA INSTEAD AND DISCOVER THE TRUTH.

WOULD I LIE TO YOU?

GRANT MORRISON
HOME, MAY '95

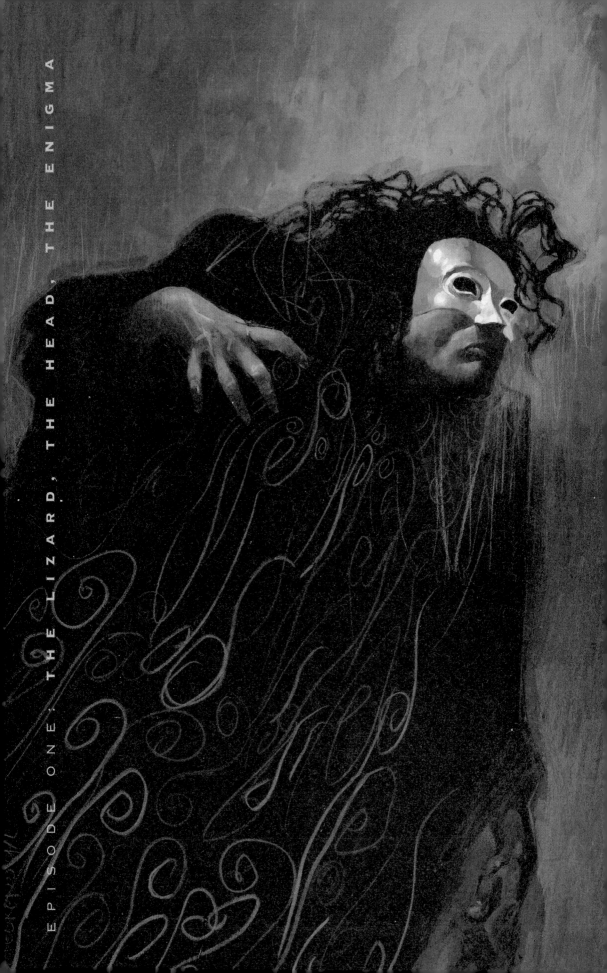

TWENTY-FIVE YEARS LATER, FIVE HUNDRED MILES DUE WEST, MICHAEL SMITH IS STARTING WHAT HE LAUGHABLY THINKS OF AS HIS "DAY"...

TONIGHT MICHAEL WILL MAKE LOVE TO HIS GIRLFRIEND, SANDRA.

HE KNOWS THIS BECAUSE TODAY IS TUESDAY.

ON TUESDAYS HE ALSO WEARS THE BLUE SOCKS AND THE GREY UNDER-WEAR AND COUNTS HIS BATH TOWELS.

HE HAS TWENTY-FIVE BATH TOWELS. BUT HOW COULD ANYONE SURVIVE WITH LESS?

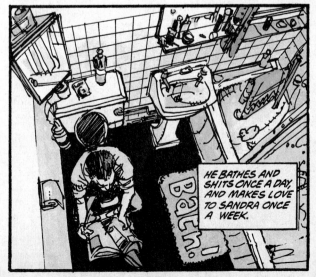

HE BATHES AND SHITS ONCE A DAY, AND MAKES LOVE TO SANDRA ONCE A WEEK.

BY EIGHT HE'S ALWAYS AT WORK, FIXING PHONES FOR THE PHONE COMPANY...

I CAN MAKE CALLS BUT CAN'T RECEIVE THEM.

WHAT'S UP, PAL? WHAT YOU LOOKING AT?

THIS ROOM... IT'S SO...

I'M SORRY, NONE OF MY BUSINESS...

NAH, YOU'RE RIGHT. IT'S A SHITHOLE. BUT WHO *GIVES* A SHIT, RIGHT?

I'LL GET THE AU PAIR TO CLEAN UP. MAYBE SHE'LL DO IT NAKED FOR ME AGAIN.

YOU EVER SEE A NAKED WOMAN VACUUM A CARPET, BOY?

AHH, NO...NO, I HAVEN'T.

YOU'RE VICTOR LAMONT, AREN'T YOU?

DING DONG

DING DONG DING DONG

SURE AM. VICTOR LAMONT. STAR OF TV AND THE BIG SCREEN.

BETCHA WISH YOU WERE ME, HUH?

MICHAEL IS A TREE APE WHO LOST MOST OF HIS HAIR AND NOW HAS NIGHTMARES ABOUT BLACK HORSES AND CANCER...

SOMETIMES HE FEELS LIKE A RUMOR DRIFTING THROUGH A WORLD OF HARD FACTS.

WHAT'S THE *POINT* OF YOU, MICHAEL?

AS THE RED LIZARD HITS THE SIDEWALK, MICHAEL IS SAYING...

BUT SANDRA, TODAY'S TUESDAY. WE NEVER GO OUT TO CLUBS ON TUESDAY. THAT'S *SATURDAY*.

JESUS, SMITHY, YOU MUST BE THE WEIRDEST BASTARD IN THE WHOLE UNIVERSE.

MIKE'S NOT WEIRD, JOE. HE'S VERY NORMAL...

YEAH, SO NORMAL IT'S WEIRD...

MAYBE *HE'S* THE *BRAIN EATER*. YOU KNOW WHAT THEY SAY ABOUT *STILL WATERS*...

LIZARD.

WHAT?

WHAT DOES "LIZARD" MEAN, MICHAEL?

I DON'T KNOW. I DIDN'T MEAN TO SAY THAT...

I MEANT TO SAY IT'S GETTING LATE. MAYBE YOU SHOULD BE ON YOUR WAY...

OH YEAH, IT'S TUESDAY, AIN'T IT? YOU TWO WILL WANT TO BE ALONE...

I'M SORRY, I DIDN'T MEAN TO TELL HER ABOUT TUESDAYS. IT JUST...

IT JUST SLIPPED...

AND IN A ROOM BELOW PACIFIC CITY, HE WAITS, SICK OF IT ALREADY BUT WITH NOTHING ELSE TO DO...

THE LITTLE MIND GAMES HE PLAYS, LIKE RECITING THE DICTIONARY BACKWARDS FROM MEMORY, FAIL TO AMUSE HIM FOR LONG.

THE WALLS OF THE WORLD HAVE BEEN TORN DOWN AND THE WIND THAT BLOWS THROUGH IS COLD AND PREPOSTEROUS.

HE CREATES A NEW LANGUAGE, A NEW GRAMMAR, EIGHT CASES AND FIVE GENDERS. THIS PASSES TWENTY MINUTES.

BOREDOM, ENNUI, ABSURDITY. HIS CLOSEST, HIS ONLY FRIENDS...

...BUT GET DRESSED...

THEN IT'S BOREDOM AGAIN...

IT LOOKS LIKE THERE'S NOTHING FOR HIM TO DO...

WHAT'S WRONG? IT'S *TUESDAY*, ISN'T IT?

I'M SORRY. GUESS I'M JUST NOT IN THE MOOD.

HOW LONG HAVE WE BEEN SEEING EACH OTHER?

HOW LONG? JEEZ, I DON'T KNOW. TWO THOUSAND YEARS, GIVE OR TAKE A COLD SHOWER...

WHY?

DUNNO. I JUST FEEL...

I DON'T KNOW. YOU KNOW I'M NO GOOD AT EXPLAINING THINGS...

SHE LIKES THE WAY HE SAYS HE'S NO GOOD AT EXPLAINING THINGS, AS THOUGH HE'S SO VERY GOOD AT EVERY- THING ELSE...

I MEAN, WHAT KIND OF PERSON IS THIS *BRAIN EATER?* WHAT TURNS ONE PERSON INTO THE BRAIN EATER AND ANOTHER PERSON INTO *ME?*

BRAIN EATER? WHY'RE YOU STILL GOING ON ABOUT THAT?

DO YOU THINK JOE'S RIGHT AND IT *IS* SOMEONE LIKE ME?

SHIT, NO. SOMEONE LIKE YOU'D NEVER DO ANYTHING AS WILD AS SUCKING SOMEONE'S BRAINS OUT...

SORRY. I DIDN'T MEAN IT LIKE THAT. WHERE'RE YOU GOING?

TELEVISION...

...SEE IF THEY CAUGHT HIM YET...

...AND JUST TO REPEAT TONIGHT'S STORY...

THE BRAIN EATER HAS STRUCK AGAIN, OUTSIDE A NIGHTCLUB IN FELGRADO HEIGHTS.

THAT MAKES TEN VICTIMS IN SEVEN DAYS. HOPE YOU SLEEP WELL TONIGHT, FOLKS...

UNCONFIRMED REPORTS ALSO HAVE IT THAT A MYSTERIOUS "MASKED MAN" WAS SIGHTED AT THE SCENE OF THE ATROCITY...

...AND NOW TODAY'S SPORTS HEADLINES...

...COME ON, MIKE, LET'S GO BACK TO BED...

FELGRADO HEIGHTS. THAT'S ONLY A COUPLE OF BLOCKS AWAY...

LET'S GO SEE WHAT'S HAPPENING...

IT'S ONE O'CLOCK IN THE MORNING, MICHAEL...

SO WHAT? PUT SOME CLOTHES ON. A MASKED MAN, SANDRA. THE BRAIN EATER.

SOMETHING BIG'S HAPPENING...

YOU'RE TELLING ME. YOU SURE YOU'RE OKAY?

SURE I AM. WHAT DO YOU MEAN?

IT'S JUST THAT... WELL...

...YOU DO SEEM A LITTLE EXCITED.

JESUS! WHERE DID THAT COME FROM?

MICHAEL WAITS FOR THE LIGHTS TO TURN GREEN, GREEN BEING HOW HE FEELS...

EVERYTHING THAT'S HAPPENING AND HE STILL HAS TO GO TO WORK.

HE COULDN'T FACE SANDRA THIS MORNING. CREPT OUT WITHOUT SAYING GOODBYE. THERE'S A DENT ON THE HOOD OF HIS CAR...

THERE'S A GREEN LIZARD FLOATING ACROSS THE ROAD.

BEEP

BEEP BEEP

BEEP BEEP

WHEN THE HONEY OF ANOTHER'S LIFE TOUCHES MY NERVOUS SYSTEM I COULD ALMOST BE SUCKING ON GOD'S LITTLE FINGER...

THE EFFECTS LAST FOR HOURS... BUT I MIGHT HAVE YOU AS WELL, JUST FOR THE SHEER *HEAD* OF IT...

DO YOU LIKE MY *LIZARD*, BY THE WAY?

TWENTY-FIVE YEARS AGO *ROGER CLIFF* WAS DRIVING THROUGH ARIZONA...

POLICE CARS AND AMBULANCES WERE CROWDED AROUND AN ISOLATED FARMHOUSE...

AS ROGER WENT TO INVESTIGATE, HE RAN OVER A SMALL RED LIZARD...

THE LIZARD WAS UNCONSCIOUS BUT ALIVE...

ROGER RESOLVED TO TAKE THE RED LIZARD BACK TO PACIFIC CITY. HEAL IT. MAKE A PET OUT OF IT.

AS SOON AS ROGER SAW THE COSTUME, HIS MIND ASSUMED THE PROPORTIONS OF AN INDUSTRIAL REVOLUTION UNAWARE OF THE ECOLOGICAL DAMAGE IT WAS CAUSING...

HIS FIRST VICTIM WAS A PRIEST.

ROGER'S SENSES WERE BLESSED WITH FURTIVE LONGINGS AND SWEET ALTAR WINE...

ROGER WAS NOW *THE HEAD.*

AND EVERYWHERE THE HEAD WENT, THE RED LIZARD WENT TOO...

BUT YESTERDAY THE HEAD UNWITTINGLY DROPPED THE LIZARD...

ALL FEAR GONE, WASHED AWAY BY THE BLOOD THAT NEVER BOILED LIKE THIS...

NOT EVEN WITH SANDRA ON THE HOOD OF HIS CAR...

NEVER SO CLOSE BEFORE. NEVER SO ANYTHING BEFORE.

HE'S STARING INTO THE EYE OF THE SUN.

THE OLD MICHAEL SMITH IS A PAIR OF TROUSERS, WORN BY ANOTHER MAN...

I KNOW WHO YOU ARE.

I KNOW WHO YOU ARE!

I...

IF IT WASN'T FOR THE FACT THAT A MONSTER CALLED THE HEAD WAS PLUNGING A METAL PIPE UP HIS NOSE PREPARATORY TO SUCKING HIS BRAINS OUT, MICHAEL SMITH COULD ALMOST LAUGH.

AT LAST HE'S GOT IT. HE'S GOT THE JOKE. THE JOKE IS LIFE.

THE PUNCHLINE IS THAT THERE ARE SO MANY THINGS HE'D LIKE TO DO WITH HIS LIFE, NOW THAT HIS LIFE IS OVER.

NOT MUCH OF A JOKE. NOT MUCH OF A LIFE. I'M DYING, HE THINKS.

NO ONE HAS EVER DIED MORE THAN THIS, HE THINKS.

JESUS CHRIST ON THE CROSS, SHAKESPEARE, JOHN F. KENNEDY, ROCK HUDSON... THEY DIDN'T DIE IN ANY BETTER OR DEEPER OR MORE REAL AND ABSOLUTE WAY THAN HE IS DYING NOW.

HE'S NEVER THOUGHT LIKE THIS BEFORE.

HE'S NEVER REALLY THOUGHT AT ALL BEFORE.

EXCEPT WHEN HE WAS A LITTLE BOY.

WHEN HE WAS A LITTLE BOY...

WHEN HE WAS A LITTLE BOY, HE HAD A LITTLE DREAM...

...ABOUT A MAN IN A MASK AND A CLOAK WHO WAS HIS MYSTERIOUS FRIEND...

GLIMPSED IN THE UNLIT ALLEYWAYS OF HIS CHILDHOOD...

FEELING ALL WARM ABOUT THOSE FARAWAY DAYS...

FORGETTING HOW LONELY, HOW MISERABLE, HOW STRANGELY DEAD HE WAS.

YOU'RE THE ENIGMA, HE THINKS...

HE'S BACK THERE NOW, THE PATHETIC LITTLE FOOL. BACK IN HIS CHILDHOOD...

FORGETTING HOW MUCH HE REALLY HATED THEM.

I KNOW WHO YOU ARE, HE THINKS. YOU'RE MY OLD SECRET PAL...

AND THEN DIES.

HE SITS QUITE STILL FOR TWO DAYS, FORGETTING TO MOVE.

REMEMBERING THE PREVIOUS TWO DAYS WITH SUCH PRECISION THAT IT TAKES FULLY TWO DAYS TO REMEMBER THEM...

REMEMBERING WITH SUCH CLARITY THAT HE FORGETS FOR A WHILE THAT THIS IS A MEMORY AND NOT THE THING REMEMBERED...

LIVING AGAIN THE MOMENT WHEN HE TOOK THE HEAD IN HIS ARMS...

WHEN HE TOOK THE HEAD IN HIS ARMS AND WONDERED...

IS THIS ENOUGH? DOES THIS MAKE IT WORTH-WHILE? DOES THIS MAKE IT LESS ABSURD?

WITH THESE ACTIONS CAN I RECREATE THE DARK AND SENSIBLE WALLS OF AN ABANDONED WELL?

HE TOOK THE HEAD IN HIS ARMS AND LOOKED INTO THE EYES, LOOKING FOR RECOGNITION, MEANING, SOMETHING...

AND, SEEING ONLY MADNESS AND DEATH...

BASHED HIS HEAD OPEN.

THE TRUTH IS SHE NEVER INTENDED, NEVER WANTED, TO END UP WITH SOMEONE LIKE MICHAEL SMITH...

THE TRUTH IS SHE'S BEEN SCREWING MICHAEL'S BEST FRIEND, JOE, ON AND OFF FOR SIX MONTHS NOW...

A RADIO PLAYS IN THE CORNER OF THE ROOM IN THE INSANE HOPE THAT THE ASININE WIT OF THE DEEJAY MIGHT JOLT MICHAEL OUT OF HIS COMA...

IT MERELY SENDS SANDRA INTO ONE...

THE TRUTH FIXES THE UNLUCKY MAN WITH A STARE OF SUCH DISMAL HONESTY...

THAT THE COMPLEX LAYERS OF LIES AND ILLUSIONS ON WHICH THE MAN'S LIFE IS BASED...

FALL AWAY, ONE BY ONE...

LEAVING IN THEIR PLACE ALL THAT IS LEFT ONCE THE LIES HAVE GONE...

...NOTHING...

YES, MY FRIENDS, I HAVE COME TO ROOT OUT DISHONESTY. I HAVE COME TO BUILD A *NEW JERUSALEM* OF TRUTH...

A DICTATORSHIP OF HONESTY...A...

FOR A MOMENT HE HESITATES, MEMORIES STIRRING...

ANOTHER LIFE, ANOTHER PERSON...

SUNTANS, LIES AND HALF-TRUTHS, A WIFE, A MISTRESS, THE CLANDESTINE CLINIC FOR COCAINE DEPENDENCY...

A PACKAGE ARRIVING ONE MORNING CONTAINING A SEE-THROUGH, A BRUTALLY HONEST SEE-THROUGH, BODY STOCKING...

...ARE STILL TRYING TO PIECE TOGETHER THE EXACT FACTS SURROUNDING LAST NIGHT'S TRAGEDY AT THE GRAPES OF WRATH RESTAURANT...

...IN WHICH *TWENTY-FIVE* PEOPLE DIED AND A FURTHER *FIFTEEN* WERE SEVERELY TRAUMATIZED...

ARTISTS IMPRESSION

...POLICE ARE NOT SAYING IF THE KILLER, INTRODUCING HIMSELF AS *THE TRUTH*, IS IN ANY WAY CONNECTED WITH *THE HEAD*, WHO WAS HIMSELF RECENTLY KILLED...

...BY A MYSTERIOUS MASKED AND CAPED VIGILANTE...

HOW WAS THE PLAY LAST NIGHT?

YET ANOTHER GLORIOUS FAILURE, I'M AFRAID.

OF COURSE, THE IDEA OF SETTING *HAMLET* IN A *BROTHEL*, WITH HAMLET AS A YOUNG PROSTITUTE WHO HAS A LESBIAN RELATION-SHIP WITH THE MADAM WAS *ALWAYS* GOING TO BE DIFFICULT TO PULL OFF...

I ONCE SAW HAMLET PLAYED ON A HUGE SPIDER'S WEB THAT COVERED THE ENTIRE STAGE. ALL THE CHARACTERS WERE FLIES, CAUGHT ON THE WEB...

OR WAS THAT *MACBETH?*

WAKE UP, SANDRA. IT'S *MORNING*. TIME TO SAY GOODBYE TO MICHAEL...

SHOULD WE SAY ANY *WORDS?* WE CAN'T JUST TURN HIM OFF LIKE HE WAS A *MICROWAVE* OR SOMETHING...

YOU CAN SAY WHATEVER PLEASES YOU, SANDRA.

OH. AHHH, RIGHT... WELL, MICHAEL...

GOODBYE, I ..I MEAN...

I KNOW YOU NEVER REALLY LIKED TALKING ABOUT *GOD* OR THAT KINDA STUFF, BUT... WELL, IF YOU'RE *LISTENING*, SIR, THIS IS MICHAEL SMITH...

HE WASN'T EXACTLY A BALL OF LAUGHS, BUT HE WAS... I GUESS HE WAS A REAL GOOD MAN...

IS THAT IT?

YES, SANDRA, THAT'S IT. MICHAEL HAS PASSED AWAY.

THE ENIGMA...

SHIT!

THE ENIGMA IS IN THE SPARE BEDROOM.

...A BIZARRE TURN OF EVENTS LEADING TO THIS SIEGE OF ACTOR *VICTOR LAMONT'S* PLUSH LAKESIDE AREA HOUSE...

OUR SOURCES SUGGEST THERE'S A REAL LINK BETWEEN *LAMONT* AND *THE TRUTH*, WHO HAS NOW CLAIMED OVER SIXTY VICTIMS...

WAIT A MINUTE...IT LOOKS LIKE THE POLICE ARE ABOUT TO MOVE IN...

HOW'S *LAZARUS?*

CUTS AND BRUISES, A LITTLE DOUBLE VISION AND NAUSEA...

APART FROM THAT, FINE...

IT'S JUST AS WELL I DECIDED NOT TO TURN HIM OFF YESTERDAY. A LESS EXPERIENCED MAN MIGHT NOT HAVE GIVEN HIM ANY CHANCE OF SURVIVAL...

YES, SIR...WELL DONE.

I *MET* VICTOR LAMONT. I FIXED HIS *PHONE.*

HIS HOUSE WAS SO MESSY I COULDN'T BELIEVE IT!

I MET HIM. THEN *I* GET ATTACKED BY *THE HEAD* AND HE BECOMES *THE TRUTH.*

HE ASKED ME IF I'D EVER SEEN A NAKED WOMAN VACUUM A CARPET.

LOOK AT ME. LOOK INTO MY EYES. SEE THE BITTER TRUTH OF YOUR LIFE REFLECTED IN THEM...

ALL THOSE LONELY NIGHTS, ALL THOSE NASTY THOUGHTS. *YOU'RE* THE ACTOR, *YOU'RE* THE ONE PLAYING A *CHARACTER* WHO IS A *LIE!*

DON'T JUST STAND THERE, SHOOT THE CRAZY MOTHER!

YOU CANNOT KILL *THE TRUTH. THE TRUTH* IS A FLAME THAT WILL NOT BE EXTINGUISHED...

YOU SAD LITTLE BOYS WITH YOUR SAD LITTLE TOYS. SEE HOW *SHALLOW* YOU ARE...

OH GOD... OH GOD, I'M SO SORRY... OH GOD, I DIDN'T WANT TO DO THAT TO YOU, FRANKIE...

IT TAKES ALL HIS WILL...

BUT THERE'S A THORN IN HIS SIDE...

HE SLOWS TO A WALK. THE THORN IN HIS SIDE, A THORN OF TRUTH THAT HE CAN'T SHAKE LOOSE...

WHAT IS HIS LIFE? DID HE WANT THIS?

THE TRUTH IS HE'LL NEVER BE THIRTY AGAIN. NEVER BE WANTED BY ANYONE THIRTY AGAIN...

THE TRUTH IS HE'D GIVE EVERYTHING, WIFE, JOB, FRIENDS, EVERYTHING, ANYTHING, TO BE THIRTY AGAIN...

THE TRUTH IS... HIS DAUGHTER...

HE LOOKS AT HIS DAUGHTER, TWENTY-EIGHT, HIS DAUGHTER...

SWIMMING IN THEIR POOL, HIS DAUGHTER...

DRYING HERSELF, SUNNING HERSELF, THE TRUTH

THE TRUTH IS HE WANTS

WHAT HE REALLY WANTS

THE TRUTH IS

OH MY GOD, A POLICEMAN'S SHOT HIMSELF!

HE JUST SHOT HIMSELF IN THE HEAD, OH MY GOD, OH MY GOD...

I DON'T KNOW WHAT'S HAPPENING HERE... THE HOUSE IS SURROUNDED WITH POLICE MARKSMEN, BUT NONE OF THEM SEEM TO BE *DOING* ANYTHING...

"...FACT IS, MOST OF THEM DON'T SEEM TO BE ALL HERE..."

TRUTH...

LOOK AT ME, *TRUTH*...

OH BOY... THIS JUST GETS *WEIRDER*...

FOR A SECOND HE FEELS ALMOST *SOLID.*

ALMOST AS THOUGH HE WERE A *REAL PERSON* IN A *REAL WORLD.*

THE ANTS SCURRYING ABOUT, BUSILY FEEDING, FIGHTING, COLLECTING, BUILDING, DYING...

THE LIZARDS WATCHING THE WORLD AS THOUGH THEY'RE WISE, BUT THEY'RE NOT WISE, JUST UGLY ENOUGH TO BE WISE...

YOU. IT IS YOU.

I KNEW IT WAS YOU...

JEEZ... THAT *IS* HIM. THAT'S THE GUY IN THE MASK...

AND THAT'S THAT *TRUTH* JERK...

GET OFF... I'VE GOT TO *LOOK* AT IT...

I'VE GOT TO SEE WHO *WINS*.

EVEN *YOU*.

EVEN *YOU* CAN BE OVERCOME...

BY THE *TRUTH*...

AND LOOK, HE'S RIGHT. THE ENIGMA IS SINKING...

SINKING IN THE BLACK AND BOTTOMLESS TRUTH OF HIS BLACK AND BOTTOMLESS EXISTENCE...

HE BROKE IN A FEW HOURS AGO AND GAVE A SERMON ON THE KIND OF TRUTHS YOU WON'T FIND IN ANY BOOK.

GOOD, BAD, OR INDIFFERENT.

THIRTY-FIVE BELIEVERS, TEN AGNOSTICS AND TWO CLOSET SATANISTS KICKED THE EUCHARIST.

AND NO ONE CAN GET NEAR THE TRUTH. NO ONE CAN FACE HIM OR IT...

SO WHERE'S THE ENIGMA?

WHAT'S HE DOING?

STILL HAVING TROUBLE WITH *THE TRUTH*, IT SEEMS.

MY GOD.

UH-UH. REMEMBER WHAT I TOLD YOU, MICHAEL. THERE *IS* NO GOD.

WHO'S THIS CREATURE MICHAEL'S WITH? AND WHAT *ABOUT* MICHAEL? NOTICE A DIFFERENCE?

DOES HE SEEM MARGINALLY LESS OF AN *ASSHOLE?*

BUT LET'S GO BACK A WEEK, TO THE HOSPITAL.

TO MICHAEL WATCHING THE ENIGMA AND THE TRUTH ON TELEVISION.

WATCHING THE ENIGMA GET TO HIS FEET, THE TRUTH CLOSING IN FOR THE KILL...

THE ENIGMA PUSHING THE TRUTH BACK, BUT ONLY JUST, BUT ONLY *BARELY* SURVIVING...

AND THEN FLOATING AWAY BEFORE THE TRUTH CAN GET ITS SHARP AND TERRIBLE VERACITIES INTO HIM AGAIN...

POOR MICHAEL. IT'S BEEN SO LONG SINCE THE POOR FOOL WAS FORCED TO REMEMBER THAT DAY, THOSE DAYS...

I'M SORRY, SANDRA, I HAVE TO FIND OUT WHO *THE ENIGMA* IS. THERE'S A CONNECTION BETWEEN THE COMIC I USED TO READ AND WHAT'S HAPPENING NOW.

WE ALL KNOW THAT. IT'S SPREAD ALL OVER THE *PAPERS*.

THE WHOLE GODDAMN *COUNTRY* IS TALKING ABOUT THIS COMIC AND THIS *ENIGMA* THING.

SOME NUTS START APING THE *SUPER-VILLAINS* FROM THE COMIC, AND SOMEONE ELSE, PROBABLY AN EVEN *BIGGER* NUT, STARTS APING THE *SUPERHERO*.

DRIVING AWAY FROM SANDRA, HE HEARD THE SOUND OF DOORS SLAMMING, BRIDGES BLAZING, OLD SKIN FLAKING, MOTHER SAYING:

BE A GOOD BOY, MICHAEL.

HE OFTEN THOUGHT OF HER. IT WAS AS THOUGH HE WOULD NEVER QUITE BE FREE OF HER...

AS THOUGH BY LEAVING HIM ON THE CORNER, SHE MADE SURE SHE WOULD NEVER LEAVE HIS MIND...

AT THE NEXT SERVICE STATION, MICHAEL VISITED THE MEN'S ROOM.

IT'S LUCKY THAT THIS IS THE KIND OF STORY THAT FOLLOWS ITS CHARACTERS INTO THE BATHROOM...

LOOK, HE'S SITTING ON THE TOILET CLUTCHING A YOU-KNOW-WHAT.

IT COMFORTS HIM. NO, DON'T LAUGH. OH ALL RIGHT, GO AHEAD, LAUGH.

HE'S READING ONE OF HIS FAVORITE PASSAGES, FROM EPISODE TWO.

WHERE HE FIRST MET THE LOVELY ENVELOPE GIRL...

SKRRRRR.

WHAT D'YOU THINK IT IS?

SOME KIND OF PARCEL. BETTER OPEN IT.

YEAH... SURE...

JEEZ... THERE'S SOMETHING *ALIVE* IN HERE...

GMMMMMM MNMMMM

WHERE AM I? WHO ARE YOU? WHERE'S VICTORIA?

WHERE'S MY *SHOW?*

I'VE GOT TO GET BACK TO MY SHOW. I'M DUE TO BE INTERVIEWED BY *ELLE.*

ENVELOPE GIRL?

HE ARRIVED AT THE ADDRESS IN ARIZONA WHERE HE USED TO SEND FANMAIL TO TITUS BIRD, WRITER AND ARTIST OF ENIGMA, BACK IN THE OLD DAYS.

A STRANGE MAN TOLD HIM TITUS HAD MOVED AND GAVE HIM AN ADDRESS OF A SMALL TOWN IN TEXAS.

SO NOW HERE HE IS. STANDING IN THE CLOTHES HE'S BEEN WEARING ALL WEEK, CREATOR-GOD OF HIS OWN LITTLE WORLD OF BACTERIA.

BUT LOOK AT THESE OTHERS. THE ENIGMATICS, THEY CALL THEMSELVES.

DID THESE APES LOSE MOST OF THEIR BRAINS WHEN THEY LOST MOST OF THEIR HAIR?

THEY CAN'T WAIT TO LEAVE THEIR PARENTS...

THEN ONCE THEY'VE LEFT THEM, CAN'T WAIT TO FIND NEW AND BIGGER PARENTS TO OBEY...

HEY! THERE HE IS!

I USED TO MAKE IT ALL UP AS I WENT ALONG, SO I DON'T KNOW WHAT WOULD'VE HAPPENED IF THE PUBLISHER HADN'T GONE BUST AND THE FOURTH EPISODE HAD COME OUT.

BUT NOW IT'S COMING BACK TO HAUNT ME. AND IF I GO BACK TO MY APARTMENT, THOSE LOONIES WILL BE WAITING FOR ME.

WHAT ARE YOU DOING?

CAUGHT A FLY.

SEE THIS? WE'RE LIKE GODS RIGHT NOW. WE HAVE THE POWER OF LIFE AND DEATH. THERE'S NO COURT THAT CAN TRY US FOR DOING WHAT WE LIKE TO THIS FLY.

THERE IS NO MORAL COME-UPPANCE. THERE IS NO GOD, EXCEPT US, HERE, NOW.

WE CAN DO WHATEVER WE LIKE.

WHY DID YOU DO THAT?

WHY NOT? I WAS BORED.

I WAS GOING TO HAVE ENIGMA SAY AND DO THAT IN EPISODE FOUR. NEVER GOT THE CHANCE.

IF YOU HAVE NOWHERE TO STAY, YOU CAN COME WITH ME.

HUH?

COME BACK TO PACIFIC CITY WITH ME.

SOMEHOW I'M MIXED UP IN WHAT'S HAPPENING. MAYBE YOU ARE TOO.

WHILE MICHAEL MEETS THE ENIGMA-MAKER, *THE TRUTH* CONTINUES TO METE OUT HONESTY TO THE LIARS OF PACIFIC CITY.

AND *THE ENIGMA* SLOUCHES IN HIS LAIR, TRYING TO COVER HIS MIND WITH A BIG SHEET OF BLACKNESS.

LATER, MICHAEL AND TITUS BREAK THEIR JOURNEY HOME AND REST IN SOME LITTLE CRAPSVILLE, U.S.A.

MY MOTHER WAS ALL RIGHT UNTIL DAD DIED, THEN SHE WENT A LITTLE STRANGE. SHE WAS INSANELY STRICT ABOUT THINGS.

EVERYTHING HAD TO BE IN ITS PROPER PLACE. EVERYTHING HAD TO BE CLEAN AND TIDY.

DAD DIED IN THE LAST BIG *EARTHQUAKE* TO HIT PACIFIC. IT WAS LIKE, AFTER THAT, MOM WAS SCARED OF ANYTHING *CHAOTIC* IN OUR LIVES.

LIKE EVERYTHING WAS ON THE EDGE OF COLLAPSING, GETTING SUCKED INTO AN EARTHQUAKE OF CHAOS.

SOMEONE, I THINK JOHN CAGE, SAID THAT LIFE WITHOUT ORDER WAS *CHAOS*, BUT ORDER WITHOUT LIFE WAS *DEATH.*

WHO'S JOHN CAGE?

IT DOESN'T MATTER.

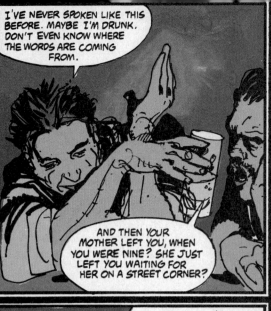

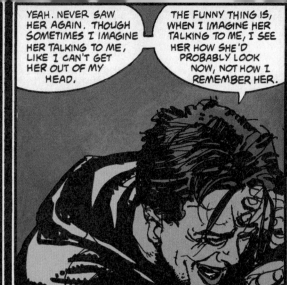

THE TRUTH? ABOUT *WHAT*?

I DON'T KNOW. ABOUT *EVERYTHING*. ABOUT THE ENIGMA.

ABOUT MY MOTHER AND WHY SHE LEFT ME. THE TRUTH ABOUT WHAT'S HAPPENING TO ME.

I'M SICK AND TIRED OF *ENIGMAS*, TITUS.

HEY, YOU CAN'T GO THROUGH...

CRKKKK

ARE YOU...

ARE YOU GOING TO KILL ME?

HIS HAND MOVES SLOWLY...

AND MICHAEL REMEMBERS THE FIRST TIME HE STOOD NAKED IN FRONT OF A STRANGE GIRL...

BECAUSE THAT'S WHAT HE FEELS LIKE NOW.

A STRANGE GIRL.

WHEN HE OPENS HIS EYES HE FINDS HIMSELF IN A NIGHTMARE WORLD SURROUNDED BY NIGHTMARE CREATURES WITH GROTESQUE OVOID HEADS AND WILDLY FLAPPING LIMBS...

MICHAEL TELLS THE POLICEMEN HE REMEMBERS NOTHING.

BUT THIS ISN'T EXACTLY THE TRUTH, IS IT, MICHAEL?

EXACTLY THE TRUTH IS BEING CARTED OUT, TO THE CHEERS OF THE CROWD, WHO OBVIOUSLY FAIL TO SEE THE IRONY OF THE TRUTH DYING IN A CHURCH...

ACTUALLY, I FAIL TO SEE THE IRONY IN THAT TOO, BUT WHO CARES WHAT I THINK?

I MEAN, DO I REALLY CARE WHAT YOU THINK? WHO ARE YOU ANYWAY?

I MEAN, ARE YOU FOLLOWING ANY OF THIS?

YOU LOOK TERRIBLE...

I HAVE TO MAKE A FEW STATEMENTS, HAVE A FEW TESTS DONE. BUT I CAN'T TELL THEM THE TRUTH, TITUS.

THEY'LL THINK I'M CRAZY...

THIS IS JOHN CADE.

JOHN'S JUST HEARD A NOISE FROM HIS FRONT ROOM, THE KIND OF SHUFFLING, SNEAKY NOISE JOHN HATES...

WHEN HE GOES TO INVESTIGATE, JOHN IS REALLY VERY, VERY DISTURBED.

SOMEONE HAS BROKEN INTO HIS HOUSE AND COMPLETELY REARRANGED THE FURNITURE.

AND AS HE LOOKS AT THE ROOM, NOW SO GROTESQUELY UN-FAMILIAR...

IT'S AS THOUGH SOMETHING BREAKS INTO JOHN'S HEAD, AND COMPLETELY REARRANGES THE FURNITURE THERE...

WHEN, ONE HOUR LATER, THE POLICE ARE CALLED BY NEIGHBORS, JOHN HAS ALREADY BEHEADED HIS WIFE AND IMPALED HIM-SELF ON THE SHARPENED LEG OF THE COFFEE TABLE.

HE'S ALSO WRITTEN SOMETHING ON THE WALL...

The Interior League

IT'S THE FOLLOWING DAY AND A LOT HAS HAPPENED SINCE JOHN CADE DE-CAPITATED HIS GOOD WIFE.

NOT ALL OF IT FUNNY.

MICHAEL GAVE STATEMENTS TO VARIOUS APEMEN BUT NEVER MENTIONED THE QUESTIONS THAT WERE INDECENTLY EXPOSING THEMSELVES TO HIS TENDER MIND...

WHAT DID THE TRUTH SEE IN ME?

WHAT IS THE TRUTH ABOUT ME?

IN THE MORNING HE WAS PICKED UP BY TITUS BIRD...

THE INTERIOR LEAGUE?

THAT'S WHAT THEY'RE CALLING THEM. HIT FIVE HOMES LAST NIGHT. TWELVE PEOPLE DEAD.

THE INTERIOR LEAGUE DIDN'T APPEAR IN YOUR COMIC, DID THEY?

NO, BUT THEY COULD HAVE. THEY'RE JUST THE KIND OF WEIRDOES I CAME UP WITH.

TV AND PAPERS ARE FULL OF IT. THEY CREEP INTO HOMES AND REARRANGE THE FURNITURE...

MY GOD! THE *MONSTERS*!

SHUT UP AND LISTEN, IT'S NOT THAT SIMPLE...

IT SEEMS THEY REARRANGE THE FURNITURE IN SUCH A WAY THAT SOMEHOW, GOD KNOWS HOW, IT DRIVES AT LEAST ONE MEMBER OF THE HOUSEHOLD *CRAZY*.

LIKE THE FURNITURE ARRANGED IN THIS PATTERN IS A KEY THAT UNLOCKS THE MIND AND...

SHIT, THOSE BASTARDS!

JESUS! WHAT'S HAPPENING?

THE *ENIGSHITTINGMATICS*... THEY'RE GATHERING IN PACIFIC...

AND THEN WHAT?

YOU SEEM A LITTLE BETTER, BY THE WAY...

HUH? YEAH. CLEAN BILL OF HEALTH. SAID I WAS LUCKY TO BE ALIVE, THOUGH. THEY SAID *THE ENIGMA* SAVED ME...

I THINK THEY'RE WRONG.

YOU REMEMBER ENVELOPE GIRL. FORMERLY KNOWN AS VICTORIA YES.

WELL, EVEN AS JOHN CADE WAS PUSHING A TABLE LEG INTO HIS HEART, SHE WAS APPROACHING AN AGING JUDGE...

WHOSE TRUSTY OLD GAVEL SEEMED TO WILT BEFORE HER NAUGHTINESS...

HE FELL, FELT HER ARMS ENVELOP HIM, GAVE HIMSELF UP TO IT, HIS OLD LIFE ESCAPING FROM SOME DUSTY DEATH ROW...

...HE AWOKE WITH THE DARKNESS SWEATING AROUND HIM, BREATHING HIS OWN AIR, HE PUSHED, UNWOUND...

AND EMERGED IN THE CLAMMY HINTERLANDS OF A LOUISIANA SWAMP...

RETURNED TO HIS PLACE, HE SITS QUITE STILL, PRETENDING HE DOESN'T EXIST, WHICH IS A HARDER GAME THAN YOU MIGHT IMAGINE. IS HE FEELING ANY BETTER?

BARELY.

IS HE FAILING? POSSIBLY. IT'S TOO SOON. MAYBE HE ISN'T TAKING IT SERIOUSLY ENOUGH. THE INTERIOR LEAGUE?

TONIGHT THE PEOPLE WILL BE AFRAID. THEY WILL CALL FOR HIM, HE WILL ANSWER. SOON.

WHEN HE KILLS ENVELOPE GIRL, WILL THE PUBLIC TURN AGAINST HIM? POSSIBLY.

THE LIZARD, A RATHER CHARMING LITTLE FELLOW WITH GREEN SPOTS AND DANCING EYES, IS PULLED BY A FORCE...

...GREATER THAN IT COULD KNOW...

AND CRUELLER.

MUCH, MUCH CRUELLER THAN ANY OF US COULD KNOW...

TITUS, YAWNING, RUBBING HIS STOMACH, SAYS...

WE'RE GOING AROUND IN CIRCLES...

...THAT'S EVERY SIGHTING OF THE *ENIGMA* AND ANYONE ELSE CONNECTED WITH HIM IN PACIFIC. ALL WE CAN DO IS WAIT...

THERE MUST BE SOME KIND OF *PATTERN*, IF WE JUST LOOK IN THE RIGHT PLACE.

WELL, YOU LOOK FOR IT. I'M GOING OUT. COMING?

NAH.

MIKE STARES AT THE MAPS FOR HOURS, TRYING TO FIND PATTERNS.

REALIZING THAT ALL HIS LIFE HE'S BEEN LOOKING FOR PATTERNS. HE WAS A PATTERNS JUNKIE.

ON THE TELEVISION THEY SPEAK OF THE GROWING PUBLIC FEAR OF THE INTERIOR LEAGUE. WHO AND WHERE WILL THEY STRIKE TONIGHT?

AND WILL *THE ENIGMA* STOP THEM?

MICHAEL TRIES TO IMAGINE WHAT IT WOULD BE LIKE NOT TO EXIST, BUT CAN'T.

THOUGH MOST OTHER PEOPLE FIND IT VERY EASY TO IMAGINE MICHAEL NOT EXISTING.

IN THE PILE OF NEWS-PAPER CUTTINGS, MICHAEL FINDS ONE OF TITUS BIRD'S MAGAZINES.

HE HATES THE WAY THE SKIN AROUND HIS BALLS TIGHTENS.

TRAITORS, HE HISSES.

HE CLOSES HIS EYES...

SLEEP CREEPS UP ON HIM LIKE A NEPHEW'S BIRTHDAY...

HELIUM BALLOONS INSIDE HIS SENSES...

FINGERS. FACE. A STRANGE GIRL.

OH MY GOD, HE THINKS. OH MY GOD.

WHAT IS THE TRUTH?

MOTHER LODE

HE GOES OUT. NEEDS AIR. LOOKING FOR TITUS, WHO'S LEFT THE NAME OF A BAR.

HE HALF EXPECTS TO SEE THE ENIGMA, IN EVERY SHADOW, IN EVERY DARK ALLEYWAY.

IN THE BAR SOMEONE PINCHES HIS BUTTOCK. NO ONE HAS EVER PINCHED HIS BUTTOCK BEFORE.

BUT NEITHER OF HIS BUTTOCKS HAVE EVER BEEN IN A BAR LIKE THIS BEFORE.

A MAN STANDS IN FRONT OF HIM, SIZING HIM UP WITH BUTCHER'S EYES...

MICHAEL MUMBLES SOMETHING AND PUSHES INTO THE BATHROOM...

WHERE HE IMMEDIATELY FEELS WORSE, SCARED LIMP TO ATTEMPT TO URINATE IN PUBLIC IN CASE HE CAN'T...

MICHAEL, HAVE YOU GONE *MAD?*

YES, I THINK I HAVE. A LITTLE. I DON'T KNOW. I WANT TO FIND OUT.

I'M SORRY, SANDRA. IT'S OVER BETWEEN US, AT LEAST FOR THE TIME BEING.

AT LEAST FOR THE TIME BEING? WHAT KIND OF *KISS-OFF* IS THAT? AND WHY ARE YOU MOVING IN WITH THIS...THIS...

HIS NAME'S *TITUS BIRD.* AND YES, HE *IS* A HOMO-SEXUAL BUT THAT HAS NOTHING TO DO WITH ANYTHING.

WE'RE STAYING TOGETHER BECAUSE SOMEHOW WE'RE LINKED.

TITUS WROTE *THE ENIGMA.* AND I THINK IN SOME WAY I'M BRINGING THE *ENIGMA* TO LIFE.

I BEG YOUR PARDON?

IT'S DIFFICULT TO EXPLAIN. TITUS THOUGHT OF IT AND WE HAVEN'T REALLY WORKED IT ALL THROUGH YET...

BUT THE BASIC IDEA IS THAT THE *ENIGMA,* AND ALL THE OTHER STUFF AROUND HIM, IS BEING CREATED BY *ME.* A *PROJECTION* OF SOMETHING INSIDE MY HEAD.

YOU KNOW HOW *POLTERGEISTS* ARE USUALLY CREATED BY THE SEXUAL TENSION IN PUBESCENT GIRLS, WELL...

HOW DID WE GET ONTO *PUBESCENT GIRLS?* MICHAEL, YOU HAVEN'T STARTED TAKING *DRUGS,* HAVE YOU?

NO. ACTUALLY, I'M JUST STARTING TO COME OFF A DRUG I'VE BEEN ON MOST OF MY LIFE...

OH *REALLY!* AND WHAT DRUG IS THAT, OH WISE ONE?

MICHAEL SMITH. MAYBE WE'LL MEET UP WHEN ALL THIS IS OVER.

BUT, MICHAEL. YOU CAN'T GO. WHAT ABOUT US?

I LOVE YOU, MICHAEL.

I DON'T THINK YOU LOVE ME, SANDRA. I THINK YOU JUST HATE THE IDEA OF *ME* NOT LOVING *YOU.*

THE ENIGMATICS, AVERAGE AGE NINETEEN, CLAIM TO HAVE FOUND A HIDDEN MESSAGE IN THE COMIC BOOK, TELLING THEM TO TAKE THEIR LIVES...

TITUS BIRD IS AT PRESENT BELIEVED TO BE IN PACIFIC CITY, AND POLICE WISH TO CONTACT HIM...

...IN A BIZARRE TWIST ON THIS MACABRE STORY, CHARLES MANSON HAS ISSUED A STATEMENT FROM PRISON, EXONERATING TITUS BIRD FROM ANY BLAME...

MANSON SAYS HE HAS READ THE ENIGMA AND CAN FIND NO HIDDEN MESSAGES IN IT...

OH, GREAT. CHARLIE MANSON IS ON MY SIDE. THINGS ARE REALLY LOOKING UP.

YOU SHOULD TURN YOURSELF IN TO THE POLICE...

SHE'S RIGHT...

AND THEN WHAT?

WELL, AHH, I GUESS THEY'LL ASK YOU A FEW QUESTIONS AND...

NO, AND THEN WHAT. THAT'S WHAT THE KID SAID BEFORE HE BLEW HIS HEAD OFF. "AND THEN WHAT."

DO WE HAVE A COPY OF EPISODE THREE BACK AT THE APARTMENT?

THE ENIGMA FOLLOWED THE RICH CAT ONTO THE ROOF OF HIS FACTORY...

THIS'LL IMPRESS YOU. IN A YEAR OR TWO I'LL BE THE OWNER OF ALL THIS. ALL THIS, MINE, ALL MINE...

AND THEN WHAT?

WELL, THEN I'LL BE TOP OF THE TREE, PULLING IN SOME REAL HEAVY DOUGH. MAYBE I'LL OWN A FEW NIGHTCLUBS, SCREW AROUND WITH A LOT OF GROOVY CHICKS, HAVE A BALL...

AND THEN WHAT?

AH, WELL, I GUESS THEN I'LL BUY A RANCH, A BIG ONE, AND BREED RACE-HORSES. SETTLE DOWN, SEND THE KIDS TO COLLEGE...

AND THEN WHAT?

AH, WELL, JEEZ, I GUESS I'LL RETIRE, YOU KNOW. SOME-WHERE WARM, MAYBE THE CARIBBEAN...

AND THEN WHAT?

WELL, HELL, I'LL JUST TAKE IT EASY, YOU KNOW...

AND THEN WHAT?

AND THEN? AND THEN, I GUESS...

I GUESS I'LL DIE...

AND THEN WHAT?

AH, SHIT, I...DON'T KNOW...

YOU KNOW WHAT IMPRESSES ME ABOUT YOU? YOUR ABILITY TO BE AS PATHETIC AS YOU ARE AND NOT WANT TO KILL YOURSELF.

IF I WERE YOU, I'D HAVE TO KILL MYSELF.

MAYBE I SHOULD KILL MYSELF. JUST LIKE THOSE KIDS. MAYBE I SHOULD SLIT MY THROAT...

SMSHHH

TITUS, FOR GOD'S SAKE...

I ONLY WROTE THE DAMN COMIC FOR A LAUGH. FOR KICKS. AND NOW OVER TWENTY YEARS LATER, HUNDREDS OF KIDS ARE DEAD BECAUSE OF ME...

NOT BECAUSE OF YOU, BECAUSE OF THEMSELVES, BECAUSE OF SOME CRAZINESS...

YOU'RE SMARTER THAN ME ABOUT THESE THINGS, TITUS. YOU KNOW THAT SOME PEOPLE COULD READ RELIGIOUS TRUTHS INTO A CORNFLAKES BOX IF THEY WANTED...

YOU'RE MAKING THIS HAPPEN. IT'S COMING OUT OF YOUR HEAD. MAYBE I SHOULD KILL YOU, MAYBE THEN IT WILL STOP!

SHIT.

I'M SORRY.

WHAT DOES IT MEAN, HUH? WHAT DOES IT MEAN WHEN THOSE KIDS DIE SO... POINTLESSLY?

IT DOESN'T MEAN ANYTHING, DOES IT? THAT'S THE SCARY PART. IF IT MEANT SOMETHING, YOU COULD HANDLE IT, BUT IT DOESN'T.

WHERE ARE YOU GOING?

OUT. NEED TO GET OUT. GET DRUNK. GET LAID.

AND THEN WHAT?

SEARCH ME.

EPISODE FIVE · LIZARDS AND GHOSTS

LOOK, THEY'RE CARRYING THE CORPSES AWAY. HO HUM.

OVER ONE HUNDRED KIDS KILLED THEMSELVES BECAUSE OF SOMETHING THEY READ IN AN ENIGMA COMIC. A SIMPLE COMIC LED TO ALL THIS.

DO I SOUND DETACHED? INDIFFERENT? I'M NOT, BELIEVE ME. I'LL TELL YOU A SECRET: I'M NOT A DISTANT NARRATOR, ALOOF FROM THE ACTION OF THIS STORY... I'M A PART OF THIS STORY.

I'M A CHARACTER IN THIS STORY. DON'T WORRY, YOU'LL UNDERSTAND EVERYTHING BY THE END, POSSIBLY EVEN BEFORE THE END. FOR NOW, LET'S TURN THE VOLUME UP...

AH! WE HEAR A VOICE! THE VOICE OF MICHAEL SMITH, SAYING...

"THERE'S NO POINT DRINKING ANYMORE, IT'S NOT GOING TO MAKE THEM COME BACK."

MAYBE NOT, BUT I'VE FOUND, DURING MY LONG AND NOT UTTERLY UNEVENTFUL LIFE, THAT IN TIMES OF GREAT EMOTIONAL UPSET AND TRAUMA, ONE CAN FIND SOME SOLACE IN THE FURRY ARMS OF ABSOLUTE INEBRIATION.

BRURUUUPP!

JEEZAS...

IT'S NOT *YOUR* FAULT THEY'RE DEAD. YOU WROTE THE COMIC, YOU DIDN'T MAKE THEM KILL THEMSELVES.

SO WHO *DID*? WHO'S TO *BLAME*?

SOCIETY?

I DON'T KNOW. THAT'S THE GREAT ENIGMA, ISN'T IT?

HAH HAH HAH

I'M SERIOUS. IT'S THE ENIGMA. WE HAVE TO FIND THE *ENIGMA*, OR WHOEVER THIS PERSON *IS* WHO'S *PRETENDING* TO BE THE ENIGMA.

YOU'RE *ENJOYING* THIS, AREN'T YOU? I'M THE SUFFERING GODDAMN ARTIST AND YOU'RE GETTING *OFF* ON IT, AREN'T YOU?

DON'T BE *STUPID*. I MEAN...

ENJOYING IT?

OKAY, THERE'S A *PART* OF ME THAT'S *ENJOY-ING* IT.

IT'S *EXCITING*. I KNOW I SHOULDN'T BE EXCITED, BUT... SHIT, I FEEL MORE ALIVE THAN I EVER HAVE. I'M SCARED, BUT ALIVE.

WHAT CAN I SAY? SHOULD I SAY I'M SORRY FOR THAT?

NO, YOU'RE RIGHT. THERE'S NO REASON TO SAY YOU'RE SORRY. SORRY'S THE WORST WORD IN THE ENGLISH LANGUAGE. NEXT TO *MODERATE*. I *REALLY* HATE THE WORD MODERATE.

TITUS, LISTEN, WE HAVE TO FIND HIM. I MIGHT BE *CREATING* ALL OF THIS, BUT UNTIL WE FIND *THE ENIGMA*, WE WON'T KNOW.

I ALSO THINK YOU SHOULD GO TO THE *POLICE*.

NO *WAY*.

WHAT CAN THEY GET YOU ON, MAN? A COMIC YOU WROTE OVER TWENTY YEARS AGO?

I KNOW HOW THEY OPERATE. THEY'LL GET THEIR *HEAD DOCTORS* STUDYING ME...

THEY'LL USE ME TO TRY TO FIGURE OUT THIS PHENOMENONEM.

IS THAT SO BAD? MAYBE THEY'LL FIND SOMETHING WE WON'T.

AND MAYBE THEY'LL CUT MY BALLS OFF FOR BEING A QUEER SEDITIOUS CULT LEADER. SOME KINDA *JIMMY JONES* WANNABE.

SHIT, WE'RE ALL OUT OF...

BHOFF!

3

HE LETS TITUS SLEEP IT OFF WHILE HE STUDIES THE PICTURES OF THE INTERIOR LEAGUE.

YOU REMEMBER THE INTERIOR LEAGUE?

THEY'VE GIVEN THEMSELVES NAMES, DAUBED ON THE WALLS OF THE HOMES OF THEIR VICTIMS.

WALL EYE. THE CARPET MAN. PRETTY AS A PICTURE.

THERE'S SOMETHING ABOUT THEM. SOMETHING FAMILIAR. A KEY, NOT TO PUT TOO FINE A POINT ON IT.

SOMETHING SIMPLE, OBVIOUS, ELUSIVE.

IT'S THE FOLLOWING DAY AND TWO MORE HOUSES HAVE BEEN REDECORATED BY THE INTERIOR LEAGUE.

FIVE PEOPLE DEAD. AND THE CITY IS BEGINNING TO ASK, WHERE IS THE ENIGMA?

MIKE AND TITUS (LET'S NOT GO INTO HIS HANG-OVER) ARE AT THE LOCAL LIBRARY.

THEY'VE FOUND A NAME.

AH, YEAH, IS THAT MISTER *CLIFF*? MISTER *BARNEY* CLIFF? I'M ENQUIRING ABOUT YOUR BROTHER, *ROGER*...

UH-HUH... UH-HUH...

I SEE. WAIT A MINUTE...

HE WANTS *FIVE THOUSAND DOLLARS*. THAT BUYS A FULL INTERVIEW. *TEN* GETS US INTO THE FAMILY ALBUM AND INCLUDES TESTIMONY FROM SOME EX-GIRLFRIENDS, PLUS HIS MEDICAL RECORDS.

CHRIST, THE PROFITEERING BASTARD!

OKAY, BARNEY, WE'LL GO FOR THE FIVE THOUSAND.

YOU'RE NOT THINKING OF *PAYING* THIS CREEP?

NO OPTION. *ROGER CLIFF* BECAME *THE HEAD*. HE WAS APPARENTLY ONE OF THE FIRST PEOPLE TO CHANGE INTO YOUR COMIC CHARACTERS. IT'S A *LEAD*, ISN'T IT?

MAYBE IT'LL LEAD US ALL THE WAY TO *THE ENIGMA*.

YEAH, BUT FIVE THOUSAND BUCKS!

IT'S NOT IMPORTANT. WHAT DOES *MONEY* MATTER NOW, ANYWAY? EVERYTHING'S CHANGED.

THE ENIGMA'S CHANGED EVERYTHING.

ONE THING I HAVEN'T BEEN ABLE TO WORK OUT IS WHERE *THE LIZARD* FITS INTO ALL THIS.

THE *LIZARD?*

FUNNY, THE POLICE NEVER ASKED ME NOTHING ABOUT THE LIZARD. WHAT'S SO IMPORTANT ABOUT THE LIZARD?

I DON'T KNOW, BUT SOMEHOW LIZARDS ARE CONNECTED TO ALL THIS, THEY'RE A CONSTANT THEME.

HOW LONG HAD ROGER HAD HIS LIZARD?

SHIT, YEARS. YEARS AND YEARS. TWENTY, MAYBE MORE. HE PICKLED IT. KEPT IT AS A KINDA *ORNAMENT,* YOU KNOW?

YOU REMEMBER WHERE HE GOT IT FROM?

WHERE? HELL, IT WAS A LONG TIME AGO.

I GUESS HE WAS OUT ON ONE OF HIS SALES TRIPS SOMEPLACE.

HOLD IT. HOLD IT ONE MINUTE... I REMEMBER NOW. THAT WAS WHY HE KEPT IT. A *MEMENTO.*

A MEMENTO OF *WHAT?*

THE MURDER. THE MURDER OUT IN ARIZONA.

"ROGER ARRIVED AS THE COPS WERE CLEANING UP. HE FOUND THE LIZARD AND KEPT IT, SO HE COULD SAY IT CAME FROM THE SCENE OF THE CRIME."

YOU'RE PROBABLY TOO YOUNG TO REMEMBER, BUT THAT KILLING MADE THE HEADLINES. TERRIBLE BUSINESS. TERRIBLE.

WHAT HAPPENED?

I DON'T RIGHTLY REMEMBER, BUT... I REMEMBER IT WAS TERRIBLE. A TRULY TERRIBLE BUSINESS.

OKAY, BOYS, THAT'S YOUR FIVE GRAND'S WORTH. NOW IF YOU'LL EXCUSE ME, I HAVE SOME HIVES TO SMOKE.

ASSHOLE.

WHAT NOW, SHERLOCK?

WE CHECK OUT THIS KILLING, I SUPPOSE. D'YOU REMEMBER IT AT ALL?

NAH, I DIDN'T TAKE TOO MUCH NOTICE OF THE NEWS BACK THEN. TOO BUSY GETTING STONED AND WRITING THE ENIGMA, WASN'T I?

HEY! WHERE'S TITUS GONE? WHAT'S HAPPENED TO HIM?

IS HE DEAD? PARALYZED FOR LIFE? ALREADY LAUGHING IT ALL OFF OR WHAT?

WHAT ARE WE DOING IN THIS SUBURBAN LIVING ROOM?

AND LOOK AT THAT FURNITURE, FOR GOD'S SAKE!

IT'S DARK OUTSIDE, WHICH USUALLY SUGGESTS IT'S NIGHT.

WAIT A MINUTE, I'LL JUST SHOW YOU SOMETHING, WHILE WE WAIT FOR THIS DOOR TO OPEN.

A PADDED CELL, THE SMELL OF STALE URINE AND STALER FOOD. HUMAN SWEAT. DEAD HAIR. FLAKES OF OLD SKIN.

YOU GET THE PICTURE.

THE BREATHING IS SHALLOW AND QUICK, LIKE A BLUNT HACKSAW BLADE SLOWLY CUTTING THROUGH LUNG TISSUE.

THE EYES BURN WITH ALL THE WET VIOLENCE OF THE YOUNG AND ALL THE DRY MALEVOLENCE OF THE OLD.

ACTUALLY THE EYES ARE ALSO A LITTLE CROOKED, THANKS TO A FAILED EYE OPERATION AS A CHILD, BUT THAT DOESN'T WORRY THIS CREATURE NOW.

THIS CREATURE WILL PLAY A BIG PART IN OUR STORY, YOU WAIT.

BACK IN SUBURBIA, THE INTERIOR LEAGUE ARE ALREADY AT WORK.

THIS IS THEIR THIRD HOUSECALL OF THE NIGHT. LOOK, THEY MOVE LIKE SLEEP-WALKERS, MECHANICAL STALKERS, NO-ONE-AT-HOME TALKERS...

MOLESTERS AND FOUL ABUSERS OF COMFY CHAIRS AND IMITATION EDWARDIAN SIDE-BOARDS, DEFLOWERERS OF TEAK COFFEE TABLES AND MEEK LANDSCAPE PAINTINGS AND...

THE ORIGINAL ENIGMA COMIC, WRITTEN BY TITUS BIRD (WHO AT PRESENT MAY OR MAY NOT BE DEAD... WHO IS, IN A SENSE, POISED BETWEEN THE TWO, IN A STATE OF MORTAL FLUX), WAS NOTED FOR ITS LACK OF ACTION.

IT TENDED TO BE A WORDY, OVERINDULGENT PIECE, HEAVILY INFLUENCED BY DRUGS AND THE MILD PARANOIA THESE DRUGS INDUCED.

IT DRIFTED TOO OFTEN INTO A RAMBLING AND MUDDLED QUASI-EASTERN SPIRITU-ALITY.

IT SOLD VERY POORLY AND WAS DISCONTINUED AFTER THREE EPISODES.

THIS OF COURSE IS NOTHING LIKE THE COMIC BOOK ENIGMA.

THIS IS REAL LIFE. OR AS REAL AS YOUR LIFE GETS, ANYWAY.

TITUS?

HOW DO YOU FEEL?

HOW DO I FEEL? JUST HUNKY-*DORY*, MAN. *YOU* SHOULD TRY GETTING YOUR ARMS AND LEGS BROKEN. IT BEATS SEX EVERY TIME.

SORRY.

YOU KNOW THE POLICE HAVE THE GUY WHO RAN YOU DOWN?

ONLY BECAUSE HE TURNED HIMSELF IN.

HE'S THE FATHER OF ONE OF THOSE KIDS THAT KILLED THEMSELVES. I DON'T BLAME HIM FOR TRYING TO KILL ME.

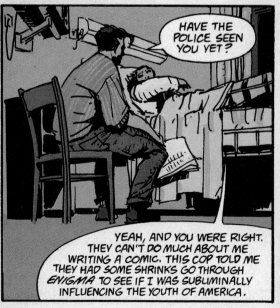

HAVE THE POLICE SEEN YOU YET?

YEAH, AND YOU WERE RIGHT. THEY CAN'T DO MUCH ABOUT ME WRITING A COMIC. THIS COP TOLD ME THEY HAD SOME SHRINKS GO THROUGH *ENIGMA* TO SEE IF I WAS SUBLIMINALLY INFLUENCING THE YOUTH OF AMERICA.

AND WERE YOU?

NAH, HE SAID THEY COULDN'T FIND ANYTHING THERE. HE ALSO SAID THE BOOK WAS A PILE OF CRAP, WHICH IS OF COURSE UNDENIABLE.

ANYTHING IN THE PAPER?

THE ENIGMA'S CAUGHT UP WITH THE INTERIOR LEAGUE. KILLED ALL THREE OF THEM LAST NIGHT.

APPARENTLY, UNTIL A WEEK AGO, THE INTERIOR LEAGUE WERE A COUNTRY AND WESTERN TRIO CALLED *THE REAL McCOYS*.

INTERIOR LEAGUE RAMPAGE ENDS

KILLED THEM, EH? DOESN'T MESS AROUND, DOES HE? YOUR ENIGMA IS MORE VIOLENT THAN MINE EVER WAS.

WE DON'T KNOW HE'S MINE. WE DON'T KNOW *HOW* I'M CONNECTED TO HIM, IF AT ALL.

YOU'RE RIGHT. MAYBE YOU'VE JUST GOT A CRUSH ON HIM.

DROP DEAD. THE MEDIA REALLY LOVE HIM. A FEW GRUMBLES IN THE LIBERAL PRESS, BUT BASICALLY HE'S A HERO.

DAMN, I WISH I KNEW WHAT IT WAS.

WHAT *WHAT* WAS?

THIS FEELING I'VE GOT ABOUT *THE INTERIOR LEAGUE.* THEY REMIND ME OF SOMETHING BUT I CAN'T PUT MY *FINGER* ON IT.

PROBABLY NOT IMPORTANT.

DID YOU CHECK OUT THAT ARIZONA MURDER?

YEAH. OLD BARNEY WASN'T WRONG.

IT *WAS* TERRIBLE.

A YOUNG WOMAN KILLED HER HUSBAND. SHE SHOT HIM IN THE FACE WITH A DOUBLE-BARRELLED SHOTGUN...

"HE MUST HAVE DIED INSTANTLY, BUT SHE KEPT RELOADING THE GUN AND FIRING AT POINT-BLANK RANGE INTO HIS FACE.

"SHE'D PUT TWENTY-TWO BULLETS INTO HIS FACE BY THE TIME THE POLICE ARRIVED."

CHRIST, WHAT DID THE POOR GUY DO TO DESERVE THAT? SQUEEZE THE TOOTHPASTE FROM THE WRONG END OF THE TUBE?

I DON'T KNOW. MAYBE IT WAS JUST ANOTHER SENSELESS KILLING. IT DOESN'T GET US ANY-WHERE, DOES IT?

I MEAN, SO ROGER CLIFF PICKS UP A LIZARD TWENTY-FIVE YEARS AGO WHERE SOMEONE GOT HIS BRAINS BLOWN OUT. WHAT'S THE CONNECTION WITH THE ENIGMA?

MICHAEL...

WHAT'S THE CONNECTION?

MICHAEL...

I'M JUST STARTING TO FEEL THAT THIS IS ONE BIG JOKE AND THERE'S NO WAY WE'LL EVER WORK OUT WHAT'S HAPPENING AND WE'LL NEVER GET TO THE ENIGMA...

MICHAEL, YOU'RE SQUEEZING MY ARM. MY ARM IS BROKEN. THEREFORE YOU ARE HURTING ME.

SHIT, I'M SORRY!

IT'S NOT LIKE YOU TO GET SO WORKED UP. GO TAKE A COLD SHOWER OR SOMETHING.

WHAT SHOULD HE DO? FLY TO ARIZONA? PUT AN AD IN THE PAPER, ASKING THE ENIGMA TO CONTACT HIM? TAKE A COLD SHOWER?

HE'S ON HIS OWN NOW. TITUS IS STUCK IN THE HOSPITAL. HE'S ON HIS OWN.

SHOULD HE LEAVE IT ALL BEHIND? GO BACK TO SANDRA, HIS FORMER LIFE, HIS OLD PAIR OF TROUSERS?

GO BACK TO HAVING SEX ONLY ON TUESDAYS, NOT AN ORGASM MORE, NOT AN ORGASM LESS?

NO. IT'S TOO LATE TO GO BACK. HE'S COME TOO FAR, CHANGED TOO MUCH.

HE'S THE WRONG SHAPE TO FIT BACK INTO HIS OLD LIFE.

ENVELOPE GIRL STILL AT LARGE

HE SUDDENLY HAS AN OVERWHELMING DESIRE TO CRAWL INSIDE ENVELOPE GIRL'S STOMACH AND CURL UP AND DREAM.

AND DREAM...

MICHAEL'S DREAM BEGINS WITH THE INTERIOR LEAGUE, DANCING LIKE PUPPETS ON HIS BED.

MICHAEL TELLS THEM TO GO AWAY...

INSTEAD THEY CHANGE INTO HIS MOTHER AND FATHER.

THERE IS A DEEP RUMBLING FROM UNDERGROUND, THE HOUSE IS SHAKING, THE HOUSE IS FALLING DOWN...

THE EARTHQUAKE BREAKS THE HOUSE IN TWO, AND MICHAEL IS PULLED FROM THE RUBBLE OF HIS CHILDHOOD BY THE ENIGMA.

SOON HE'S STANDING IN A ROOM FULL OF DOLLS AND MORE PUPPETS. ENVELOPE GIRL OPENS HER ARMS, SUCKING HIM IN.

HE STEPS TOWARDS HER, AND WHAT WILL HE FIND BEHIND THE FOLDS OF HER IMPISH SMILE?

BUT SUDDENLY SHE IS HOLDING A BUCKET OF WATER.

SHE LAUGHS AND

SLOSHHH

MICHAEL IS WET. THE SHEETS ARE HOT AND STICKY, GLUED TO HIS LEGS. HE HASN'T DONE ANYTHING LIKE THIS SINCE HE WAS A BOY.

HIS HEAD IS STILL GIDDY WITH SILLY DREAM THOUGHTS.

AS THE WATER SCALDS HIS BOYISH SHAME AWAY, THOUGHTS OF ENVELOPE GIRL IN THE ROOM FULL OF DOLLS AND PUPPETS RISE LIKE STEAM AND CLOUD HIS VISION.

ALLOWING HIM, PARA-DOXICALLY, TO SEE.

SHIT. THAT'S IT. PUPPETS, DOLLS.

I'VE BEEN THERE.

TWENTY MINUTES LATER, MICHAEL'S OUTSIDE THE PACIFIC FOLK MUSEUM.

AND ONLY NOW DOES HIS EXCITEMENT FADE. SO WHAT IF HE DREAMT ABOUT A ROOM IN THIS MUSEUM?

SINCE WHEN DO DREAMS COME TRUE? AND WHAT IF SHE IS IN THERE? WHAT WOULD THAT MEAN?

THAT HE'S PSYCHIC? THAT SOMEONE WANTS HIM TO MEET ENVELOPE GIRL AND CAN CONTROL HIS DREAMS?

THE THOUGHT OF THE WORD CONTROL REMINDS MIKE OF THE SHEETS LYING IN THE LAUNDRY BAG BACK AT THE APARTMENT, AND HIS TOTAL LACK OF IT.

CONTROL, THAT IS, CONTROL.

YOU ALL WANT TO BE WRAPPED UP. YOU'RE ALL SUCH LITTLE BOYS.

JESUS, YOU'RE REALLY HERE!

OF COURSE I'M HERE. I'VE ALWAYS BEEN HERE, THERE, AND EVERYWHERE.

COME HERE, LITTLE BOY...

NO, WAIT, I'M DIFFERENT. I'M A PART OF THIS TOO. I DREAMT YOU'D BE HERE.

SO WHAT DO YOU WANT, A MEDAL?

BUT IT'S...IT'S INCREDIBLE. IT'S SIGNIFICANT.

TAH DAH!

DIDN'T HEAR YOU DRIVE UP. CAR BROKEN DOWN?

AH, NO, NO, NOT REALLY.

WELL, YOU'RE LUCKY. THIS IS PRIVATE LAND AND IF YOU'D DRIVEN UP IN A CAR, I'D HAVE SHOT YOUR TIRES OFF.

WHERE IS THIS?

WHERE? THE COLLINS RANCH, WHAT'S LEFT OF IT.

IS THIS... IS THIS ARIZONA?

SURE. ARIZONA, PLANET EARTH.

WHERE DID YOU PARK YOUR SPACESHIP, BOY?

THIS IS WHERE... THIS IS WHERE THE *MURDER* WAS.

THIS IS WHERE THAT WOMAN SHOT HER HUSBAND, ISN'T IT?

YEP. THIS IS WHERE ELLEN BLEW JIMMY'S HEAD OFF.

YOU *KNEW* THEM?

SURE I KNEW THEM. JIMMY WAS MY *COUSIN*.

I HAD TO TRY TO IDENTIFY HIS BODY MYSELF, AND...

WHAT'S IT TO YOU, ANYHOW? YOU ONE OF THEM SICKOES, IS THAT IT?

NO. IT'S COMPLICATED. I'M... I'M DOING SOME RESEARCH. I'M SORRY IF I BROUGHT BACK ANY BAD MEMORIES...

LET'S GET OUT OF THIS SUN.

THIS PLACE HASN'T BEEN LIVED IN SINCE IT HAPPENED. PEOPLE THOUGHT IT WAS *HAUNTED.* THOUGHT THE GHOST OF *JIMMY* WAS STILL HERE.

MUST ADMIT, I'VE SEEN A FEW ODD THINGS HAPPEN AROUND HERE MYSELF.

ODD? LIKE WHAT?

OH, I DON'T KNOW. *THINGS,* YOU KNOW. UN-NATURAL THINGS. SAW A *FLYING LIZARD* HERE ONE TIME. NEARLY GAVE ME A GODDAMN HEART ATTACK, IT DID.

WHAT'S WRONG, BOY? YOU LOOK LIKE YOU PISSED YOURSELF OR SOME-THING.

A FLYING LIZARD? YOU SAID YOU SAW A *FLYING LIZARD?*

YEP. I WOULDN'T BELIEVE IT MY-SELF IF I HADN'T SEEN IT.

I *BELIEVE* YOU, IT'S JUST...

SO WHAT'S HAPPENED? WHAT ARE YOU DOING HERE NOW?

FIXING IT UP. DECORATING IT SO I CAN GET RID OF THE PLACE. THERE HAVEN'T BEEN ANY MORE HAUNTINGS SINCE THE EXORCISTS CAME.

HOLD IT, HOLD IT, EXORCISTS? WHAT *EXORCISTS?*

THE ONES WE GOT IN LAST YEAR TO GET RID OF JIMMY. WORKED, TOO. ANOTHER BEER, BOY?

HE FINDS THE MOUTH OF A TUNNEL BENEATH A DEAD CAR AND STARTS TO CRY AGAIN.

THIS MOUTH WAS ONCE CRUEL TO HIM, YOU SEE. IT SENT HIM AWAY WITHOUT SO MUCH AS A GOODBYE KISS, AND NOW IT HISSES...

" I REMEMBER *YOU.* YOU'RE THAT LITTLE PANTS-PISSER MICHAEL SMITH. THIS USED TO BE YOUR *HOME.*

"THIS USED TO BE YOUR SAD LITTLE *WORLD,* WHICH HAS THANKFULLY ENDED. *HAH HAH HAH.*"

AND AS HE DIGS DOWN INTO THE FISH BONES AND BAKED BEAN CANS OF THE PAST, HE REMEMBERS TALKING TO TITUS, EARLIER THIS FINE DAY.

POOR OLD TITUS BIRD, ALL BENT AND BORED.

MICHAEL PHONED HIM FROM THE AIRPLANE, WHICH SEEMED A FITTINGLY UNLIKELY PLACE FROM WHICH TO HOLD A CONVERSATION...

HOW THE HELL DID YOU END UP IN ARIZONA?

THROUGH THE *LOVELY ENVELOPE GIRL'S* BELLY, ACTUALLY. I TALKED TO A RELATIVE OF THE GUY WHO WAS *KILLED* THERE, YOU REMEMBER...

YEAH, YEAH, THE GUY WHOSE FACE WAS SHOT OFF BY HIS WIFE. SO WHAT?

SO EVERYTHING. I THINK... I THINK THAT PLACE, MAYBE THAT MURDER, IS AT THE *HEART* OF WHAT'S HAPPENING.

THE OLD MAN MENTIONED A *GHOST*, AND *EXORCISTS*, AND *FLYING LIZARDS*. AND ANOTHER THING...

I KNOW WHAT IT WAS ABOUT *THE INTERIOR LEAGUE*, THE THING I COULDN'T REMEMBER.

THE ONE CALLED *WALL EYE*. HIS... COSTUME. THE *PATTERN* ON IT.

I'VE SEEN IT BEFORE. A LONG TIME AGO.

A LONG TIME AGO...

OH YES, HE CAN SMELL IT, AFTER ALL THESE YEARS.

MOM'S TERRIBLE COOKING...

...THE OLD MAN'S ROTTEN PIPE TOBACCO...

DAD?

OH MY GOD...

DAD!

THE END OF THE WORLD...

OUT! IT'S A QUAKE!

OH,
JESUS...

THIS WAS WHERE I *LIVED* WHEN I WAS A *CHILD.*

MY FATHER DIED HERE IN THE LAST BIG EARTHQUAKE TO HIT *PACIFIC.* HIS BODY WAS NEVER RECOVERED, SO THIS WAS HIS *GRAVE.* MY MOTHER LAID FLOWERS ON THE GROUND ABOVE HERE...

"SEAGULLS FLEW OFF WITH THEM, BEFORE THE CRAPPY LITTLE MAKESHIFT SERVICE WAS EVEN FINISHED. EVERYTHING WAS AGAINST US.

"*MY POOR OLD DAD. THE GROUND SWALLOWED HIM AND THEN THE SKY STOLE HIS FLOWERS. POOR OLD DAD.* "

I LOST MY *ENIGMA* COMICS TOO. THEY WERE BURIED WITH HIM AND I USED TO IMAGINE HIM LIKE AN EGYPTIAN PHARAOH, BURIED WITH WHAT HE NEEDED FOR THE AFTERLIFE, READING *THE ENIGMA* FOR ALL ETERNITY.

I HAD TO BUY *NEW* COPIES, OF COURSE.

IT WAS THE *WALLPAPER* THAT MADE ME REMEMBER, FINALLY. THE WALLPAPER WE USED TO HAVE HERE IN OUR *LIVING ROOM.*

THE SAME AS THE *COSTUME* THAT *WALL EYE* WORE. BUT I DON'T UNDERSTAND HOW THAT COULD BE. THERE'S STILL AN AWFUL LOT I DON'T UNDERSTAND.

AN *AWFUL* LOT.

AH, HE FEELS AS THOUGH HE IS STANDING ON THE VERY EDGE OF A HIGH MOUNTAIN.

PART OF HIM WISHES HE COULD FALL FROM IT. HE'S NEVER REALLY FALLEN BEFORE, HE'S ALWAYS PULLED BACK AT THE LAST MINUTE.

BECAUSE, ACCORDING TO POPULAR OPINION, WHEN YOU FALL FROM A MOUNTAIN, YOU USUALLY END UP GETTING HURT.

THIS MAN IS GOING TO BE HURT. HE WON'T DIE BUT HE'LL NEVER WALK OR WORK AGAIN.

HE ALWAYS SAID HE WANTED MORE TIME TO READ.

THIS IS THE CREATURE WHO'LL GIVE HIM THAT TIME.

YOU REMEMBER THIS CREATURE? THIS CROSS-EYED, CRAZY THING?

TO CATCH THE MEREST WHIFF OF ITS MADNESS IS TO UNDERSTAND WHY SMALL STICKY BOYS PULL THE WINGS OFF FLIES.

IT'S SO DEEP, SO DEFINITE, SO UN-IMAGINATIVE...

SO BRUTAL...

SO ATTRACTIVE.

PERHAPS.

WHAT ARE YOU DOING IN MY OLD HOME? IS THIS A *COINCIDENCE?* I MEAN...WHERE DO I FIT IN? WHAT ABOUT *TITUS?* AND THE *LIZARDS?*

HOW IS ALL THIS HAPPENING? *ENVELOPE GIRL, THE HEAD,* IT'S *CRAZY...*

LOOK, I'M TOO TIRED TO BE SCARED OF YOU. I'VE COME ALL THIS WAY... JUST TO END UP WHERE I STARTED, MOM AND DAD'S FRONT ROOM, TALKING TO... TO THE HERO FROM MY *FAVORITE COMIC!*

NOW... *SAY SOMETHING!*

COME WITH ME.

SOME OF YOU MIGHT WANT TO TURN AWAY AT THIS POINT AND DISCUSS SOMETHING ELSE AMONGST YOURSELVES...

THE LOVELY ENVELOPE GIRL AWAITS YOU! ARE YOU READY TO BE UTTERLY SENT?

NO.

OHH... OHH UGHHH...

HE WANTS TO TURN AWAY, BUT CAN'T, BUT MUST WATCH...

NO! GET AWAY!

AIEEEEE!

HER CRIES ARE LIKE THE SHRIEKS OF FAT SEAGULLS, CARRYING WITHERED FLOWERS FROM A RUIN.

OH GOD MY STOMACH... WHAT HAVE YOU DONE TO MY STOMACH...

ENVELOPE GIRL!

VICTORIA!

LOOK AT THEM, THE SPELL BROKEN, RETURNED TO SENDER, SICK AND DISGUSTED...

ALL OF WHICH MEANS NOTHING TO HIM.

GO ON, KILL HER. SHE'S ONLY MAKE-BELIEVE.

YOU BASTARD. YOU VICIOUS BASTARD.

...ENVELOPE GIRL, REAL NAME VICTORIA YES, THE SUPERMODEL FROM LONDON, ENGLAND, IS NOW IN A HOSPITAL. DOCTORS SAY HER CONDITION IS CRITICAL BUT STABLE.

MEANWHILE, THE EXACT WHEREABOUTS OR IDENTITY OF THE ENIGMA REMAINS, WELL, AN ENIGMA.

BUT IN A NEW OPINION POLL CONDUCTED FOR PACIFIC NEWS THIS EVENING, SIXTY PERCENT OF YOU THOUGHT THE ENIGMA SHOULD BE ARRESTED, AND ONLY TWENTY WERE IN FAVOR OF HIM, A SWING OF SOME THIRTY POINTS...

AMATEUR FILM

BASTARD.

YEAH, PACIFIC NEWS? THIS IS TITUS BIRD, CREATOR OF THE ENIGMA COMICS. I'D LIKE TO GIVE AN INTERVIEW, THAT'S RIGHT.

I WANT TO PUBLICLY DISASSOCIATE MYSELF FROM THE THUG MASQUERADING AS MY CHARACTER.

AND SOON THE SKY CLOSED AND I WAS IN THE WORLD IN THE DARK, THE ONLY, THE ONE TRUE WORLD.

I SCREAMED FOR A WHILE. SCREAMED FOR GOD. BUT GOD HAD LEFT THE WORLD. I WAS ALONE. WITH THE VOICES AND THE OTHERS.

"SOON I BECAME HUNGRY AND ASKED FOR FOOD WITH MY MIND."

"AND FOOD CAME."

FOOD CAME. IT WAS A GOOD WORLD, A PERFECT WORLD, A WORLD WITHOUT GOD BUT PERFECT ALL THE SAME.

I DON'T UNDERSTAND. WHAT'S THIS GOT TO DO WITH THE MURDER? WHAT WAS THIS WORLD YOU WERE IN?

THE WORLD. THE ONLY WORLD. THE WORLD.

THAT'S ENOUGH FOR NOW. IT'S YOUR TURN.

MY TURN?

"TO TELL ME ABOUT ONE WORLD ENDING... AND ANOTHER BEGINNING."

Pacific City
200 miles

HOW DOES HE FEEL? DIZZY? SICK AND DIZZY? HE KNOWS WHAT THE ENIGMA WANTS HIM TO TALK ABOUT. HOW DOES HE KNOW?

HE KNOWS THAT THE ENIGMA KNOWS WHAT HE IS HIDING.

WHAT ARE YOU HIDING, MICHAEL SMITH?

ALL RIGHT, I'LL TALK. I THINK THIS IS WHAT YOU MEAN. A FEW NIGHTS AGO I WENT OUT LOOKING FOR TITUS AND FOUND MYSELF IN A GAY BAR. NEVER BEEN IN ONE BEFORE.

SOMEONE PINCHED MY ASS.

"I FLED TO THE BATHROOM AND STAYED IN A STALL AS I TRIED TO GATHER MY THOUGHTS. I HAVEN'T TOLD TITUS THIS. DON'T KNOW WHY NOT, BUT..."

"EVENTUALLY I LEFT THE BATHROOM. AND THIS GUY JUST KIND OF STOOD IN FRONT OF ME."

"HE TOLD ME HIS NAME WAS STEPHEN. I SAID THAT MINE WAS...WAS TITUS."

"HE WAS ONLY A YOUNG GUY. MAYBE THAT MADE IT EASIER."

HE KNOWS, HE KNOWS EVERYTHING, BUT STILL HE SAYS:

EASIER TO DO WHAT, MICHAEL?

EASIER... TO SAY YES.

WHEN HE ASKED ME BACK TO HIS APARTMENT.

"I'D HAD A FEW DRINKS BUT I CAN'T BLAME IT ON THAT. I STOOD IN THIS GUY'S APARTMENT AND, YES, IT WAS LIKE HAVING THE WORLD FALLING APART AROUND ME.

"I WAS IN AN EARTHQUAKE AGAIN.

"HE'D KISSED ME IN THE ELEVATOR.

"I'D LET HIM KISS ME. I'D WANTED HIM TO KISS ME."

HE WENT TO FIX SOME DRINKS AND THEN SOMETHING BROKE, MY NERVE PROBABLY, I DON'T KNOW, AND I RAN OUT, CAUGHT A CAB HOME.

I COULDN'T SLEEP. I WAS SCARED. SHAKING. SICK.

EXCITED?

YEAH. YEAH, EXCITED. BUT A LITTLE DISGUSTED BY MY EXCITE-MENT. I MEAN, I WASN'T GAY! WHAT WAS I DOING?

SO I LAY IN BED, WANTING SLEEP, WANTING OBLIVION. I TRIED SOMETHING I USED TO DO WHEN I WAS A KID AND I COULDN'T SLEEP. I MASTURBATED.

WHILE I DID I TRIED THINKING ABOUT WOMEN, TO CHASE STEPHEN'S KISS AWAY, YOU KNOW, NASTASIA KINSKI, MADONNA, THIS BLACK GIRL I SEE AT THE SUPERMARKET, EVEN SANDRA, MY EX-GIRLFRIEND.

BUT THE WOMEN KEPT FADING AWAY.

BUT IT WASN'T *STEPHEN* WHO TOOK THE WOMEN'S PLACE. IT WASN'T STEPHEN I KEPT SEEING. IT WAS *YOU.*

I KEPT THINKING OF, I KEPT SEEING, YOU.

AND AFTERWARDS I FELT SICK, WITH FEAR AND SHAME, AND I COULDN'T EVEN TALK ABOUT IT TO TITUS, TITUS OF ALL PEOPLE, WHO'D HAVE UNDERSTOOD.

YOU KNOW, I'VE DREAMT ABOUT YOU SO OFTEN. THE DREAMS DISTURB ME BUT I DON'T WANT THEM TO STOP.

IT SEEMS YOU'RE RUNNING THROUGH ALL MY LIFE. ALL MY PAST AND PRESENT. TELL ME SOMETHING...

DOES *ANYTHING* MEAN *ANYTHING?* I MEAN, IN THE END, DOES IT REALLY MATTER WHAT WE DO? DOES IT MAKE ANY DIFFERENCE?

DOES ANYTHING REALLY MATTER?

NO. NOTHING REALLY MATTERS.

GOOD.

AND HE FEELS HIMSELF FALLING.

AS THOUGH FALLING FROM THE HIGHEST MOUNTAIN.

AND THIS TIME HE WILL LET HIMSELF FALL.

AND HE WILL LEARN...

HE WILL LEARN THAT, CONTRARY TO POPULAR OPINION...

IT NEEDN'T HURT AT ALL.

EPISODE SEVEN: SEX IN ARIZONA

YES.

YES, THEY'VE DONE IT, ON THE ROOF AND BACK HERE, AT HOME.

MICHAEL SMITH AND THE ENIGMA. MICHAEL SMITH AND HIS SECRET CHILDHOOD COMIC BOOK PAL.

IT WASN'T A SMOOTH OPERATION. A LOT OF FUMBLING, DEAD ENDS, FALSE STARTS, BUT WHAT THEY LACKED IN TECHNIQUE THEY MADE UP FOR IN FEELING.

YES, REALLY. FEELING. THESE AREN'T TREES OR FISH, AFTER ALL. THESE ARE WARM CREATURES, WITH WARM SKIN. THESE ARE CREATURES WHO HAVE TAKEN THE BIOLOGY OUT OF SEX.

THESE ARE TWO MEN REDRAWING THE MAPS OF THEMSELVES.

ACTUALLY YOU SHOULD HAVE SEEN IT. YOU REALLY MISSED SOMETHING.

I STILL DON'T *GET* IT THOUGH. I MEAN, I STILL FIND IT ALL VERY *ENIGMATIC.* TITUS BIRD, THE GUY I TOLD YOU ABOUT, HAD A *THEORY.*

ARE YOU LISTENING?

POSSIBLY.

HE THOUGHT THAT MAYBE *I* WAS CREATING IT ALL.

YOU?

IT'S ALL COMING OUT OF MY MIND. SOMETHING TO DO WITH THE *REPRESSION* I'M PRONE TO. SOMEHOW I'M MAKING THE COMIC BOOK HE WROTE COME TO *LIFE.*

I MADE THE SUPER-VILLAINS. THE HEAD, THE TRUTH. ALL THE OTHERS. AND MOST OF ALL I MADE *YOU.*

AND SEEING AS YOU'RE HERE IN BED WITH ME, OR AT LEAST YOU WERE A FEW SECONDS AGO, MAYBE THIS MEANS THAT I CREATED IT ALL JUST TO...

SHIT, I DON'T KNOW. TITUS CAME UP WITH THE IDEA, NOT ME.

IT'S BRILLIANT.

BUT?

NOT TRUE.

WOULD YOU *KNOW* IT'S NOT TRUE? IF I CREATED YOU, I MEAN.

OF COURSE I KNOW IT'S NOT TRUE.

I CREATED *MYSELF.*

IT REALLY HAPPENED.

WHAT DOES *THAT* MEAN? WHAT ABOUT THE *FARM?* THE *COLLINS FARM.* YOU TOLD ME HOW YOUR MOTHER... HOW SHE DROPPED YOU INTO A *WELL.*

DID THAT REALLY HAPPEN OR WAS IT JUST... A *STORY...*

BUT YOU'RE NOT GOING TO TELL ME ANY MORE UNTIL YOU FEEL LIKE IT.

THAT'S RIGHT. ARE YOU HUNGRY?

YEAH, ACTUALLY...

NO. NO, I'M NOT HUNGRY.

AFTER YOU'VE... EATEN, THERE'S SOMETHING I WANT YOU TO HELP ME WITH. IT'S NOT STRICTLY LEGAL BUT... I'VE A FEELING THAT WON'T BOTHER *YOU.*

AND... HOW, HOW ARE YOU FEELING NOW, MAN?

GOOD, I THINK. SCARED SHITLESS BUT GOOD. THERE'RE LOTS OF THINGS I'D LIKE TO ASK YOU... ABOUT... YOU KNOW...

YEAH, LATER. FIRST... I MEAN, WHAT HAVE YOU TWO BEEN *DOING* THESE PAST FEW DAYS...

OH, TALKING. SLEEPING. THE OTHER THING. GETTING TO KNOW EACH OTHER.

WELL, *HE'S* BEEN GETTING TO KNOW *ME*, AT LEAST.

THIS IS INCREDIBLE. SO WHO *IS* HE? WHAT'S THE BIG SECRET? WHAT HAS BEEN *HAPPENING*?

WELL, I THINK WE CAN SCRAP YOUR THEORY ABOUT IT ALL BEING A PRODUCT OF MY SICK AND ANAL MIND, BUT...

I DON'T KNOW YET. HE'S TOLD ME A LITTLE. I THINK HE WANTS ME TO BE ABLE TO TAKE IT IN, BIT BY BIT, WITHOUT IT BLOWING MY MIND.

WHAT HE *HAS* TOLD ME IS UNREAL. IT'S WILDER THAN ANYTHING *YOU* COULD HAVE WRITTEN.

THANKS A MILLION, BUDDY.

WANNA DROP OF POISON?

I DIDN'T MEAN TO DENIGRATE YOUR WRITING SKILLS.

THAT'S GOOD. BECAUSE I DON'T HAVE ANY.

NOT TRUE, BUT LISTEN TO THIS. HE LIVED DOWN A WELL. I THINK FOR A VERY LONG TIME.

A WELL? YOU MEAN A BASEMENT APARTMENT?

NO, A WELL, AS IN A WELL. AND YOU KNOW THAT WOMAN AND THE MAN SHE MURDERED AT THE RANCH IN ARIZONA? HIS PARENTS.

HIS MOTHER DROPPED HIM IN THE WELL AFTER HE DID SOMETHING TO HIS DAD. SOMETHING TO HIS DAD'S FACE.

THAT MUST BE WHY SHE KEPT SHOOTING INTO IT, TO HIDE WHAT THE ENIGMA HAD DONE TO IT.

BE CAREFUL, MIKE. I DON'T TRUST HIM. YOU SAW WHAT HE DID TO ENVELOPE GIRL.

I KNOW. I KNOW THIS IS DANGEROUS.

BUT I CAN'T STOP THINGS NOW. I'VE NEVER FELT LIKE THIS ABOUT ANYONE BEFORE. NEVER FELT ABOUT ANYTHING LIKE THIS BEFORE.

YOU CAN'T GO IN THERE,

BUT IT'S *VICTORIA* YES. SHE WAS *ENVELOPE GIRL.* I'VE MET HER, BEFORE SHE WAS HURT. I HELPED SAVE HER AND I REALLY HAVE TO SEE HER.

AND I WILL REALLY HAVE TO BREAK YOUR HEAD IF YOU DON'T GET...

WHAT'S HAPPENED TO HIM? IS HE SLEEPWALKING OR SOMETHING?

SEARCH ME. WANNA GO FOR IT?

WHY NOT?

VICTORIA.

VICTORIA, ARE YOU AWAKE?

OH JESUS.

HOW DID *YOU* GET IN HERE?

THAT DOESN'T MATTER. WHY DID YOU WANT TO MEET ME HERE?

SO YOU CAN HELP HER.

HMMM... WILLY?... WILLY, I SIMPLY *CAN'T* WEAR THIS THING...

WHY SHOULD I HELP *HER*?

YOU *HURT* HER. I THINK YOU CAN HELP HER. YOU HELPED *ME* ONCE, DIDN'T YOU? WHEN I ALMOST DIED. IT WAS *YOU* WHO BROUGHT ME BACK TO LIFE, WASN'T IT?

THAT WAS DIFFERENT.

WHY WAS THAT DIFFERENT?

BUT MORE THAN THAT I WANT YOU TO *WANT* TO HELP. I WANT HER TO *MEAN* SOME-THING TO YOU.

YOU *WANT* ME TO HELP HER?

YES.

I'LL HELP HER... BUT WHY SHOULD SHE MEAN ANYTHING TO ME? IF SHE WERE A LIZARD I'D EAT HER AND THINK NOTHING OF IT.

SHE SHOULD MEAN SOMETHING BECAUSE... BECAUSE SHE'S A *HUMAN PERSON* AND...

HEY, BERTRAND RUSSELL...

JUST BLOODY-WELL LET HIM HELP ME AND SAVE THE PHILOSOPHY TILL LATER, OKAY, DARLING?

WHAT'S HE DOING?

DON'T KNOW. KEEP QUIET, HE MIGHT NEED TO CONCENTRATE.

AHHH... THAT FEELS... ALL FUNNY...

SHE'S PASSED OUT. SHE'S ALL RIGHT NOW. I'M SUPPOSED TO FEEL *GOOD* ABOUT THAT, AM I?

I THINK I'M *MISSING* SOMETHING.

MICHAEL, THERE'S NOTHING HERE. NO SCAR. THEY SHOWED THE SCAR ON T.V. IT WAS A MONSTER.

HE GOT RID OF IT. HE *CURED* HER!

I BET YOU CAN DO ANYTHING YOU WANT. YOU COULD BE A *SAVIOUR!* YOU COULD BE *JESUS!* MY CHARACTER, THE ENIGMA. *JESUS! THE MESSIAH!*

TAKE IT EASY, TITUS. YOU'RE SOUNDING LIKE AN *ENIGMATIC.*

I'M *SERIOUS.* HE'S NOT HUMAN, NOT HUMAN LIKE *US.* HOW DO WE *KNOW* HE'S NOT JESUS?

WELL, FOR A START BECAUSE I *SLEPT* WITH HIM. IF JESUS CAME BACK IS IT VERY LIKELY THAT I'D END UP *SLEEPING* WITH HIM?

YES! WHY NOT? WHY SHOULDN'T THE NEXT MESSIAH BE GAY?

THIS IS GETTING SILLY. HE'S...

SHIT!

ENIGMA? YOU ACTUALLY CALL HIM *ENIGMA*?

ENIGMA?

SHUT UP.

ENIGMA, WHAT'S WRONG?

CLOSE. SHE'S CLOSE. GO. MUST GO. NOW. TOO SOON.

WHAT'S CLOSE?

I DON'T LIKE THIS. IF SOMETHING THAT CAN SCARE *HIM* IS CLOSE I MOST DEFINITELY DON'T LIKE IT.

WHO ARE YOU? WHAT AM I DOING SURROUNDED BY THESE GHASTLY PEOPLE?

OH.

SOMETHING HURTS INSIDE.

AIEIEEEEE

UHH UHH UHHHH

ARE YOU DOING THIS? MAKE IT STOP! FOR GOD'S SAKE!

NO. MUST LEAVE, NOW...

AIEIEIEIEI

VICTORIA!

YOU'RE THE ENIGMA! DO SOMETHING!

BUT HE CAN'T. HE'S AS HELP-LESS AS WE ARE. DOOMED TO WATCH THE STORY UNFOLD.

A SMELL ENTERS THE ROOM. THE SMELL OF SEX.

THE SMELL OF SEX IN ARIZONA.

IF SUCH A THING EXISTS.

THIS IS MORE LIKE IT!

A FIGHT SCENE!

ENIGMA VERSUS HIS MOM! JESUS VERSUS THE VIRGIN.

MAYBE TITUS BIRD WOULD HAVE HAD A SCENE LIKE THIS IF HE'D BEEN ALLOWED TO PRODUCE PART FOUR OF THE ENIGMA.

OR MAYBE NOT.

UGHHHH!

OH GOD...

YOU'VE KILLED HIM! YOU'VE KILLED YOUR OWN SON!

MOTHER WALKS THROUGH THE RATHER EMBARRASSED STREETS, REMEMBERING A TIME SOME TWENTY-SIX YEARS AGO. HAVING SEX.

IN ARIZONA.

THEY WEREN'T MARRIED YET, WHICH MADE IT A LITTLE MORE EXCITING: SIN SEEMS TO PUT THE GAS INTO ORGASM.

AND AS SHE HAD SEX IN ARIZONA HER MIND DRIFTED ONTO OTHER THINGS.

WE'LL NEVER KNOW EXACTLY WHAT THINGS. PEOPLE MOVE IN AND OUT OF OTHER PEOPLE'S LIVES, AND NO ONE EVER KNOWS EXACTLY WHAT OTHER PEOPLE ARE THINKING.

IN THIS WAY WE ARE ALL ALONE. BUT I AM MORE ALONE THAN MOST.

IT'S SAFE TO SAY, THOUGH, THAT EVEN BEFORE THEIR HASTILY ARRANGED MARRIAGE TOOK ALL THE SIN AND ALL THE GAS AWAY, SEX IN ARIZONA HAD LEFT THEIR LIVES...

HAD PACKED ITS BAGS AND CAUGHT A BUS TO THE BRIGHT LIGHTS OF THE CITY.

...AND SAW THE
NEW WORLD.

REMEMBER HOW YOUR
MIND SCREAMED AND
DARKNESS COVERED
YOU AGAIN?

HE'D BEEN IN THE CLINIC A LITTLE OVER AN HOUR AND THEY HAD CONDUCTED A NUMBER OF TESTS, ALL OF WHICH HE HAD DILIGENTLY FOULED UP.

HE HATED THESE GHASTLY CREATURES, WITH BODIES SIMILAR TO HIS OWN BUT WITH OVAL BLOBS IN PLACE OF THE PANORAMA THAT CROWNED HIS OWN BODY.

IT TOOK A LITTLE WHILE TO REALIZE THAT HE WAS LIKE THEM: THAT HE TOO HAD AN OVAL BLOB, WITH EYES AND MOUTH; THAT THE WORLD DIDN'T SIT ON HIS SHOULDERS.

PUT HIM DOWN, THAT'S RIGHT, NICE AND EASY...

WHAT... WHAT'S GOING ON?

THAT'S WHEN THE DRIPPING, ISOLATED HORROR BEGAN.

THAT'S WHEN HE THOUGHT OF THE WALLS OF HIS WARM WELL...

I THINK OUR... FRIEND WAS ABOUT TO EAT YOU.

OF HIS PERFECT LITTLE WORLD IN ARIZONA THAT HAD BEEN BLOWN APART.

THESE PEOPLE DISGUSTED HIM. THEY WERE LITTLE CLEVERER THAN LIZARDS BUT THOUGHT THEMSELVES SO BRILLIANT.

THEY WEREN'T BRILLIANT. THEY WERE HORRIFICALLY DULL.

THEY WERE THE SMALL NOISE AN INSECT MAKES WHEN IT SLIDES DOWN YOUR THROAT.

I CAN'T IMAGINE... HOW TERRIBLE IT MUST HAVE BEEN. IT'S SURPRISING YOU DIDN'T GO COMPLETELY INSANE.

YOU'RE *NOT* COMPLETELY INSANE, ARE YOU?

I'M THE SANEST MAN IN THE WORLD.

I'M GLAD YOU CAN TELL ME ABOUT IT. I WANT TO HELP.

DON'T LOOK AT ME AS THOUGH *I'M* INSANE. YOU KNOW HOW I FEEL ABOUT YOU. IT'S ONLY NATURAL FOR ME TO WANT TO HELP.

JUST LIKE *YOU'RE* HELPING *ME*, NOW.

ARE WE NEAR?

VERY NEAR.

NOT EXACTLY A SALUBRIOUS NEIGHBORHOOD, IS IT?

I DON'T KNOW WHAT YOU MEAN. PARK HERE. WE'LL WALK.

AHH, HOW DID YOU, YOU KNOW... FIND... THE CEMETERY?

I THREW MY MIND OUT. I FOLLOWED LIFELINES, OLD AVENUES, DEAD VOICES. I OPENED MY NOSTRILS AND INHALED.

RIGHT. SO YOU DIDN'T TRY THE LOCAL LIBRARY FIRST THEN?

HE MADE IT BACK TO THE BOTTOM OF THE WELL. BUT IT WAS NO GOOD. HE KNEW THERE WAS A WORLD OUTSIDE.

THIS KNOWLEDGE WAS LIKE AN ALIEN MONSTER FROM A FIFTIES' SCIENCE FICTION MOVIE, RUNNING AMOK ACROSS A BURNING PLANET.

AND HE SAT THERE IN THE DARK, A MAN WHO KNEW THAT STEVE McQUEEN WAS DEAD AND THAT NOTHING COULD SAVE THE WORLD NOW.

EVENTUALLY HE ARRIVED IN PACIFIC CITY.

GIRLS
LIVE XXX
LOVE ACT
ACTION XXX
ALL NIGHT!
LIVE SHOW
VIDEO
GIRL
XXX XXX

AT NIGHT HE WALKED ALONG FLORENCE BEACH, SUMMONING PRETTY LIZARDS WHO FLEW MYSTERIOUSLY THROUGH THE AIR TOWARDS HIM.

ANY OLD FRIENDS HERE? NO.

HE MISTOOK FOR SIMPLE CITY GRIME THE LITTLE LIZARDS' SHEEN OF URBAN GRANDEUR.

SO HE WOLFED DOWN A FEW OF THEM IN DISGUST, MASSACRED THE REST WITH A TWITCH OF HIS BROW, AND DEPARTED.

I THINK WE SHOULD JUST BE SILENT FOR ONE MOMENT HERE, AND CONTEMPLATE THIS WASTE OF REPTILIAN LIFE.

EXCUSE ME, ARE YOU STILL THERE? I HAVEN'T LOST YOU YET, HAVE I?

HOW COULD YOU UNDERSTAND WHAT THE DOCTORS WERE SAYING? I THINK WE CAN SAFELY ASSUME YOU DIDN'T HAVE ANY *FORMAL* EDUCATION.

I'D HEARD VOICES ALL MY LIFE. I'D ALWAYS THOUGHT THEY WERE A PART OF MY WORLD. I LEARNED QUICKLY TO UNDERSTAND THEM.

OF COURSE NOW I KNOW I WAS SIMPLY HEARING THE OUTSIDE WORLD TALKING.

AND THEN YOU FOUND OUR OLD HOUSE?

I WAS LOOKING FOR SOMEWHERE... DEEP. DEEP AND SOLITARY.

"I SENSED A HOLE IN THE GROUND, SENSED THAT IT HAD ONCE BEEN A HOME, A LITTLE WORLD THAT HAD ALSO BEEN BLOWN APART.

"I ALMOST FELT NOSTALGIC.

"IT DIDN'T TAKE LONG TO DIG MY WAY DOWN.

"I KNEW I COULD NEVER BE CONTENT AGAIN BUT I NEEDED SOMEWHERE TO STAY.

IT'S ALL HOLES TODAY, HE THINKS, IN THAT ODD, IRRELEVANT WAY HUMANS HAVE OF THINKING WHEN THEY'RE FACING SOMETHING PARTICULARLY BIG.

THE HOLE WHERE THE ENIGMA LIVED, THE HOLE THAT WAS MICHAEL'S OLD, BURIED HOME...

AND NOW THIS HOLE, STUFFED WITH DEAD BODIES, ONE OF WHOM GAVE BIRTH TO MICHAEL, A LONG TIME AGO.

"BE A GOOD BOY, MICHAEL," HE REMEMBERS HER SAYING, AS SHE WALKED AWAY INTO HISTORY AND MYTH.

I KNOW I'VE SAID SOME HARD THINGS ABOUT MICHAEL, BUT HE IS TAKING THIS RATHER WELL, ISN'T HE?

OOPS!

SPOKE TOO SOON!

I NEVER THOUGHT I'D CRY. THOUGHT I'D BE ANGRY AND RANT AND RAVE OR SOMETHING, BUT... WHAT HAPPENED TO YOU AFTER YOUR MOTHER LEFT?

IT IS? SHIT. THAT'S... I MEAN, WHY? WHY WOULD YOU WANT TO...

BECAUSE I SAW THAT MY LIFE WAS ABSURD.

I KNEW IT DIDN'T MATTER WHAT I DID, BUT I HAD TO DO *SOMETHING*.

I HAD TO TRY TO REBUILD THE WALLS OF MY WELL, OR STARE INTO THE ABYSS AND GO INSANE.

SO I THOUGHT, WHAT MORE ABSURD WAY TO LIVE YOUR LIFE THAN TO BASE IT ON THIS ABSURD LITTLE COMIC BOOK?

I SIMPLY ADJUSTED MY FACE A LITTLE TO LOOK LIKE THE ENIGMA. I RECREATED MY OWN FEATURES TO GIVE MYSELF A BETTER LIKENESS.

THE CHARACTERS OF THE COMIC WOULD BE MY NEW WALLS. I WOULD HAVE THE PARAMETERS I REQUIRED.

I WOULD BE *THE ENIGMA*.

AFTER HE READ THE COMICS HE SENT HIS MIND OUT, OUT PAST THE VACANT LOTS AND DERELICT STOREFRONTS...

OUT THROUGH THE STREETS AND HOUSES, THE DISTRICTS OF PACIFIC CITY.

AND THEN FURTHER...

OUT ACROSS THE DESERTS OF CALIFORNIA, THROUGH THE COUNTRY MUSIC RADIO WAVES, THE SMELL OF YUCCAS, THE DRY MOJAVE.

OUT, FURTHER OUT, HE PUSHED HIS MIND...

WHILE HE SAT IN MICHAEL SMITH'S OLD HOME, SHIVERING WITH FEAR, BECOMING SMALLER AS THE ARC OF HIS MIND GREW LARGER, TRAVELLED FURTHER.

NOTHING WOULD STOP HIS MIND.

IT TRAVELLED OUT ACROSS THE CENTRAL PLAINS OF THE UNITED STATES...

THE WHITE DESERTS OF THE NORTH, THE VAST OCEANS...

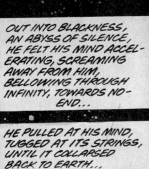

OUT INTO BLACKNESS, AN ABYSS OF SILENCE, HE FELT HIS MIND ACCELERATING, SCREAMING AWAY FROM HIM, BELLOWING THROUGH INFINITY, TOWARDS NO-END...

HE PULLED AT HIS MIND, TUGGED AT ITS STRINGS, UNTIL IT COLLARSED BACK TO EARTH...

AND ALIGHTED IN *DOUG MOON'S FAMILY TAILORS,* IN AN EASTERN SUBURB OF PACIFIC CITY.

FOR SOME REASON DOUG WOULD NEVER UNDERSTAND (HE WOULD SHORTLY FORGET ABOUT IT ANYWAY), HE WAS SUDDENLY COMPELLED TO BEGIN WORK ON A NUMBER OF OUTLANDISH SUITS.

THE ENIGMA'S MIND WAS SLOWER NOW AS IT LOCATED A PICKLED LIZARD THAT STILL HAD ARIZONIAN GRIT ON ITS PICKLED BELLY.

WITH A STRANGE YEARNING FOR HIS WELL AND FOR HIS LIZARDS, HE MADE THIS LIZARD SPEAK TO A MAN CALLED ROGER CLIFF, WHO WAS ABOUT TO HAVE HIS LIFE CHANGED IN A BIG WAY...

ROGER, YOU WILL FIND A PACKAGE WAITING FOR YOU AT LOCKER NUMBER EIGHT IN WEST PACIFIC STATION...

MY MOTHER...WAS THE GOD WHO DROPPED ME DOWN INTO THE WORLD.

IT SEEMS MY GOD LOST HER MIND AND WAS INCARCERATED IN AN ASYLUM.

WHEN I LEFT MY WORLD AND BEGAN STRETCHING MY MIND OUT, SHE WOKE, SHE SENSED MY MIND AND SHE GREW STRONG BECAUSE OF IT, FEEDING ON IT, ALLOWING IT TO UNLOCK SOME LATENT POWER WITHIN HERSELF.

SHE IS AN ECHO OF WHATEVER I AM. YOU COULD SAY I AM GIVING BIRTH TO MY OWN MOTHER.

WELL, SHE SAID TO MEET HER HERE. AND CHRIST, I ALMOST HAD A HEART ATTACK WHEN I SAW THAT BIG UGLY MOTHER PRANCING AROUND MY APARTMENT, WITH HER BIG HORRIBLE...

OH, SORRY, I FORGOT. I GUESS THAT *IS* YOUR *MOM* I'M TALKING ABOUT.

DON'T WORRY ABOUT HIM. HIS FEELINGS AREN'T EASILY HURT.

IN FACT, I DOUBT WHETHER HE HAS ANY FEELINGS AT ALL.

WHAT ARE YOU TALKING ABOUT? I THOUGHT YOU AND HIM...

HE THREW HIS MIND INTO HIS VICTIMS SO HE COULD TWIST AND MUTILATE THEIR BODIES AND MINDS.

SO THEY WOULD FIT INTO THE *"WORLD"* HE WAS BUILDING FOR HIMSELF.

I WOULDN'T BE *THE ENIGMA* WITHOUT THE ENIGMA'S SUPER-VILLAINS.

JESUS! THEY WERE *REAL PEOPLE*, GOING ABOUT THEIR *LIVES*.

WHAT AM I DOING WITH YOU? I'M IN LOVE WITH A *MONSTER!*

I'M IN LOVE WITH A MONSTER? BOY OH BOY, *I* COULD HAVE WRITTEN THAT LINE.

WHOSE SIDE ARE YOU ON?

THE SIDE OF TRUTH AND JUSTICE, MY BOY.

WHEN I SAW THE WORLD THAT I WAS GOING TO HAVE TO INHABIT I ALMOST FAINTED.

IT WAS LIKE YOU WAKING UP AND FINDING YOURSELF IN A WARD FULL OF FROTHING IDIOTS, AND KNOWING THAT YOU WOULD HAVE TO SPEND THE REST OF YOUR DAYS WITH THEM.

SEE THAT LIZARD, THE GREEN, PLUMP ONE? IMAGINE IF HE HAD A HUMAN'S INTELLIGENCE. IMAGINE IF HE KNEW THIS ENTIRE STORY...

BUT COULD ONLY COMMUNICATE IT TO THE MINUSCULE BRAINS OF HIS FELLOW LIZARDS.

WHAT ARE YOU DOING?

LOOK AT HIM. LOOK AT THE *NIGHTMARE* HE HAS WOKEN TO.

THAT'S HOW *I* FELT.

I'M SORRY... MAYBE I'M JUST TOO MUCH OF A FROTHING IDIOT TO UNDERSTAND. ALL I KNOW IS THAT DOING THOSE THINGS TO PEOPLE IS WRONG.

THAT WORD *"WRONG"* AGAIN. HOW ARE YOU DEFINING...

I DON'T KNOW! I DON'T CARE ABOUT CLEVER WORDPLAY OR SEMANTICS. TO ME IT'S IMPORTANT THAT I KNOW THAT SOME THINGS ARE JUST WRONG. PERIOD.

WITHOUT IT... WE MIGHT AS WELL JUST PACK OUR BAGS AND GO HOME. WITHOUT IT WE'RE NOT HUMAN. OR NOT HUMAN *ENOUGH.*

TAKE YOUR MASK OFF, PLEASE. I'D LIKE TO SEE YOU WITHOUT YOUR MASK.

LOOK, MAYBE I'LL JUST...

NO, STAY. YOU'VE BEEN AN IMPORTANT PART OF THIS JOURNEY.

DO YOU REMEMBER IN THAT BAR, WHEN YOU INVITED ME BACK TO THE ROOM FOR SEX? WHEN YOU THOUGHT I WAS GAY?

AND YOU PUNCHED ME AND SAID YOU WEREN'T QUEER.

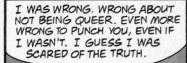

I WAS WRONG. WRONG ABOUT NOT BEING QUEER. EVEN MORE WRONG TO PUNCH YOU, EVEN IF I WASN'T. I GUESS I WAS SCARED OF THE TRUTH.

YOU KNOW, THERE'S ONE THING THAT I CAN'T QUITE WORK OUT. I DIDN'T WRITE ABOUT THE INTERIOR LEAGUE.

HE'D RUN OUT OF YOUR SUPER-VILLAINS SO HE HAD TO MAKE SOME UP HIMSELF.

I WAS WRONG TO SAY SORRY FOR MAKING A PASS. I SHOULD HAVE PUNCHED YOU BACK.

WE WERE BOTH GOOD PAVLOVIAN DOGS, WEREN'T WE? DRIBBLING ON CUE. BARKING TO ORDER.

SHIT, I CAN'T STAND TENSION. THAT'S WHY I MADE SURE MY COMICS NEVER HAD ANY.

HOW LONG WILL WE HAVE TO WAIT?

NOT LONG. I CAN FEEL HER APPROACHING.

AND THEN WHAT?

THAT'S A VERY GOOD QUESTION. AND THEN WHAT?

SHE WANTS TO *DESTROY* ME, AS SHE THOUGHT SHE DID AFTER I CHANGED MY FATHER'S FACE AND SHE SHOT HIM DEAD.

SHE'S STRONG ENOUGH TO DO IT. SHE FEEDS ON WHAT I AM AND SHE BECOMES STRONGER THAN ME.

THEN WHY ARE WE HANGING AROUND HERE? SHOULDN'T WE BE IN A FAST CAR SOMEWHERE?

NO. NO RUNNING. NOW IS THE TIME. NOW IS THE TIME TO SEE IF IT HAS WORKED.

IF WHAT HAS WORKED?

WHY ARE YOU LOOKING AT ME LIKE THAT? TO SEE IF *WHAT* HAS WORKED?

IF *YOU* HAVE WORKED, MICHAEL.

EVEN AS ROGER CLIFF'S HEAD SWELLED LIKE THE VIRGIN MARY'S BELLY, THE PERSON WHO WAS NOW THE ENIGMA WAS MAKING A DISCOVERY.

A CROSS-EYED, MAD CREATURE WAKING IN HER CELL...

HE KNEW THEN THAT SHE WOULD COME AFTER HIM, KNEW THEN THAT SHE WOULD DEFINITELY DESTROY HIM.

UNLESS...

HE SENSED THE DEVOTIONAL SWEAT OF THE LITTLE BOY'S FINGERS THAT HAD ONCE FONDLED THESE PAGES.

THE PICTURES HAD BEEN WORN INTO THE SHAPE OF THE EYES THAT ONCE SWEPT OVER THEM, TIME AND AGAIN, LIKE A ROCK FASHIONED BY WATER.

HE FOUND THE LITTLE BOY, OLDER NOW BUT ESSENTIALLY UNCHANGED. MICHAEL SMITH. YES. HE WOULD BE PERFECT. MICHAEL WAS THINKING ABOUT HIS NEXT JOB, IN A SWANKY PART OF TOWN.

A PACKAGE FOLLOWED HIM TO VICTOR LAMONT'S PALATIAL EGO. THE PACKAGE CONTAINED THE SUIT OF THE TRUTH.

AND NOW, ALL THIS TIME LATER, THE TRUTH IS WHAT MICHAEL IS LEARNING.

WHY?

SO YOU THREW YOUR MIND INTO ME? YOU CHANGED ME JUST AS MUCH AS YOU CHANGED VICTORIA YES AND ROGER CLIFF?

YOU MADE ME GO *QUEER* SO I'D FALL IN *LOVE* WITH YOU.

MY ONLY CHANCE WAS TO BE A LITTLE MORE... HUMAN. TO FEEL A LITTLE LOVE AND COMPASSION, AND HOPE MY MOTHER WOULD DRAW ON THIS TOO, AND SPARE ME.

YES.

ALL THAT CONFUSION, ALL THAT SUFFERING, ALL THOSE CHANGES. YOU *ORCHESTRATED* IT...

I'M SORRY. I DON'T WANT TO HURT YOU. IT WAS WRONG OF ME.

I'LL CHANGE YOU BACK.

WHAT?

I'LL UNDO THE CHANGES. I'LL MAKE YOU AS YOU WERE BEFORE.

I THINK HE'S OFFERING TO *DE-HOMOSEXUALIZE* YOU, MICHAEL.

NO.

NO?

GOOD BOY.

IT DOESN'T MATTER HOW OR WHY I HAD THOSE EXPERIENCES, WHETHER IT WAS SOMETHING WITHIN ME OR YOU CHANGING ME...

THIS IS HOW I AM NOW. AND I LIKE MYSELF THIS WAY. I FEEL COMFORTABLE THIS WAY.

SO I'LL STAY AS I AM.

I THINK I'M HAPPY AS I AM.

AHH, CHAPS...

WE HAVE COMPANY.

IT'S TOO LATE. I'VE FAILED.

SHE'LL DESTROY ME.

MAYBE NOT. YOU DIDN'T *HAVE* TO OFFER TO CHANGE MIKE BACK. YOU DID THAT BECAUSE OF YOUR *FEELINGS* FOR HIM. AND I SAW THE WAY YOU LOOKED AT HIM JUST NOW.

IT'S BEEN A FEW YEARS SINCE ANYONE'S LOOKED AT *ME* LIKE THAT.

SHE'S WAITING. STAY HERE WHILE I GO AND MEET HER.

NO, WE'RE IN THIS TOGETHER, WE'LL ALL GO.

YOU WITH US, TITUS?

WHY THE HELL NOT?

I DON'T KNOW HOW THE STORY ENDS.

THEY WALKED HAND IN HAND DOWN THE HILL TOWARDS HIS MOTHER.

THEY WALKED OUT OF MY LIFE AND INTO THEIR FUTURES.

THAT'S ALL I KNOW.

BUT YOU DON'T LISTEN, DO YOU? YOU SQUAT THERE WITH YOUR DULL EYES. YOU SQUAT THERE AS THOUGH YOU WERE WISE.

BUT YOU'RE NOT WISE.

YOU'RE JUST UGLY ENOUGH TO BE WISE.

LOOK, LET ME START AGAIN. AND TRY TO CONCENTRATE THIS TIME.

YOU COULD SAY IT ALL STARTED IN ARIZONA.

TWENTY-FIVE YEARS AGO. ON A FARM...

ALSO AVAILABLE FROM VERTIGO

TRADE PAPERBACKS

ANIMAL MAN
MORRISON/TRUOG/GRUMMETT/HAZLEWOOD
INTRODUCTION BY GRANT MORRISON

BLACK ORCHID
GAIMAN/MCKEAN
INTRODUCTION BY MIKAL GILMORE

BREATHTAKER
WHEATLEY/HEMPEL
INTRODUCTION BY NEIL GAIMAN

THE BOOKS OF MAGIC
GAIMAN/BOLTON/HAMPTON/VESS/JOHNSON
INTRODUCTION BY ROGER ZELAZNY

THE BOOKS OF MAGIC: BINDINGS
RIEBER/AMARO/GROSS
INTRODUCTION BY JANE YOLEN

BREATHTAKER
WHEATLEY/HEMPEL
INTRODUCTION BY NEIL GAIMAN

DEATH: THE HIGH COST OF LIVING
GAIMAN/BACHALO/MCKEAN
INTRODUCTION BY TORI AMOS

DOOM PATROL: CRAWLING FROM THE
WRECKAGE
MORRISON/CASE/HANNA/VARIOUS
INTRODUCTION BY TOM PEYER

HELLBLAZER: ORIGINAL SINS
DELANO/RIDGWAY/VARIOUS
INTRODUCTION BY JAMIE DELANO

HELLBLAZER: DANGEROUS HABITS
ENNIS/SIMPSON/PENNINGTON/SUTTON
INTRODUCTION BY GARTH ENNIS

JONAH HEX: TWO-GUN MOJO
LANSDALE/TRUMAN/GLANZMAN
INTRODUCTION BY JOE R. LANSDALE

THE SANDMAN: PRELUDES AND NOCTURNES
GAIMAN/KIETH/DRINGENBERG/VARIOUS
INTRODUCTION BY F. PAUL WILSON

THE SANDMAN: THE DOLL'S HOUSE
GAIMAN/DRINGENBERG/M. JONES III/BACHALO/
ZULLI/PARKHOUSE
INTRODUCTION BY CLIVE BARKER

THE SANDMAN: DREAM COUNTRY
GAIMAN/VARIOUS
INTRODUCTION BY STEVE ERICKSON

THE SANDMAN: SEASON OF MISTS
GAIMAN/K. JONES/DRINGENBERG/
M. WAGNER/M. JONES III /GIORDANO/PRATT/MCKEAN
INTRODUCTION BY HARLAN ELLISON

THE SANDMAN: A GAME OF YOU
GAIMAN/MCMANUS/VARIOUS
INTRODUCTION BY SAMUEL R. DELANY

THE SANDMAN: FABLES AND REFLECTIONS
GAIMAN/VARIOUS
INTRODUCTION BY GENE WOLFE

THE SANDMAN: BRIEF LIVES
GAIMAN/THOMPSON/LOCKE
INTRODUCTION BY PETER STRAUB

THE SANDMAN: WORLDS' END
GAIMAN/VARIOUS ARTISTS
INTRODUCTION BY STEPHEN KING

SANDMAN MYSTERY THEATRE:
THE TARANTULA
M. WAGNER/DAVIS
INTRODUCTION BY DAVE MARSH

V FOR VENDETTA
A. MOORE/LLOYD
INTRODUCTIONS BY DAVID LLOYD AND ALAN MOORE

PRESTIGE FORMAT BOOKS

MERCY
DEMATTEIS/P. JOHNSON

ROGAN GOSH
MCCARTHY/MILLIGAN

GRAPHIC NOVELS

TELL ME, DARK
K. WAGNER/WILLIAMS

THE MYSTERY PLAY
MORRISON/MUTH

HARDCOVERS

THE HEART OF THE BEAST
MOTTER/S. PHILLIPS

UPCOMING TRADE PAPER-
BACK COLLECTED EDITIONS

HELLBLAZER: FEAR AND LOATHING
MR.PUNCH
VAMPS

UPCOMING HARDCOVER
COLLECTED EDITIONS

THE SANDMAN: PRELUDES & NOCTURNES
THE SANDMAN: THE DOLL'S HOUSE
THE SANDMAN: DREAM COUNTRY
THE SANDMAN: THE KINDLY ONES